Strategies To Achieve Reading Success

STARS™ Series
Book
5

W9-BKM-340

CURRICULUM
ASSOCIATES®, Inc.

ISBN 0-7609-0699-8
©2000—Curriculum Associates, Inc.
North Billerica, MA 01862

15 14 13 12 11 10 9 8 7 6 ·

TABLE OF CONTENTS

PART ONE: LEARN ABOUT MAIN IDEA

Read this paragraph about bats. As you read, think about the most important idea in the paragraph.

Why Bats Can Fly in the Dark

Sometimes, people say that someone who doesn't see well is "as blind as a bat." Bats, however, are not really blind. Most of them have tiny eyes that cannot see very well in the dark. So, bats rely on their ears to "see" at night. Bats make high squeaking noises as they fly. These sounds spread out through the air like waves. When the sounds hit an object, they bounce back as echoes. The bats' large ears easily pick up the echo sounds to locate objects in their path. This is called echolocation. Bats use echolocation to hunt and to avoid bumping into things in the dark!

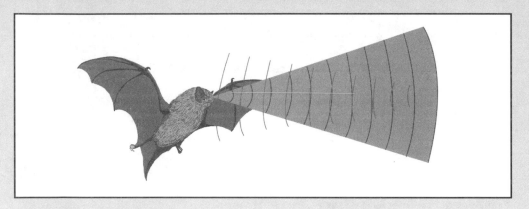

The last sentence of the paragraph states the most important idea.

Bats use echolocation to hunt and to avoid bumping into things in the dark!

The most important idea in a paragraph is called the **main idea**.

The main idea tells what a paragraph is mostly about.

★ The main idea is sometimes found in the first sentence of a paragraph.

★ The main idea is sometimes found in the last sentence of a paragraph.

★ The main idea is sometimes not found in any one sentence. You can figure out the main idea by asking yourself, "What is the most important idea in the paragraph?"

Read this e-mail letter. As you read, think about the main idea of the letter. Then answer the questions.

Tamara,

Today I learned some odd facts about United States geography. For example, do you know the answer to this question: What state lies the farthest south? Most of the kids in my class answered "Florida." A few kids said "Texas." My response was "California." We were all wrong. The most southern state is Hawaii. We also learned that Alaska is both the most western and the most eastern state. Its Aleutian Islands extend really far to the west. They actually cross the line that divides the Eastern and Western hemispheres. Another interesting thing I learned is that parts of Virginia are farther west than West Virginia. Also, did you know that parts of Wisconsin, which is in the Midwest, are farther east than parts of Florida?

Reply soon!

Robin

1. What is the main idea of the paragraph?
   Ⓐ The state that lies farthest south is Hawaii.
   Ⓑ Robin's entire class answered a geography question incorrectly.
   Ⓒ Robin learned some odd facts about United States geography.
   Ⓓ Parts of Wisconsin are farther east than parts of Florida.

2. Where or how did you find the main idea?
   Ⓐ in the first sentence of the paragraph
   Ⓑ in the last sentence of the paragraph
   Ⓒ in the middle of the paragraph
   Ⓓ by thinking about the most important idea in the paragraph

 Work with a partner. Talk about your answers to questions 1 and 2. Tell why you chose the answers you did.

Remember: The main idea tells what a paragraph is mostly about.

★ Read the first sentence of the paragraph. The main idea is sometimes found here.

★ Read the last sentence of the paragraph. The main idea is sometimes found here.

★ Sometimes, the main idea is not found in a sentence from the paragraph. You can figure out the main idea by thinking about the most important idea in the paragraph.

Read this fable by Aesop. As you read, ask yourself, "What is the fable mostly about?" Then answer the questions.

The Prophet

A prophet sat in the marketplace and told the fortunes of all who cared to use his services. Suddenly, someone came running up to the prophet. The man reported that the prophet's house had been broken into by thieves. They had stolen everything they could lay their hands on.

The prophet rushed off, tearing his hair and cursing the criminals. The witnesses to this scene were much amused. One of them said, "Our friend claims to know what will happen to others. It seems, however, that he's not clever enough to see what's in store for himself."

3. What is the fable mostly about?
   Ⓐ a prophet who worries too much
   Ⓑ a busy marketplace
   Ⓒ a prophet who has been robbed
   Ⓓ a prophet who cannot predict his own future

4. Where or how did you find the main idea?
   Ⓐ in the first sentence of the paragraph
   Ⓑ in the last sentence of the paragraph
   Ⓒ in the middle of the paragraph
   Ⓓ by thinking about the most important idea in the paragraph

Look at the answer choices for each question. Read why each answer choice is correct or not correct.

3. What is the fable mostly about?

   Ⓐ a prophet who worries too much

   This answer is not correct because there is not enough information in the fable to support this idea. The prophet was upset when he heard that he had been robbed. However, this reaction is typical of someone who has been robbed. This does not mean that the prophet worries too much.

   Ⓑ a busy marketplace

   This answer is not correct because the marketplace, the fable's setting, is only one detail in the fable. It is not the most important idea.

   Ⓒ a prophet who has been robbed

   This answer is not correct because this is only one idea in the fable, not the most important idea.

   ● a prophet who cannot predict his own future

   This answer is correct because it tells what all the sentences in the fable are mostly about. It is the most important idea.

4. Where or how did you find the main idea?

   Ⓐ in the first sentence of the paragraph

   This answer is not correct because the first sentence tells where the prophet was and what he was doing. This is not the most important idea in the paragraph.

   ● in the last sentence of the paragraph

   This answer is correct because the last sentence states that the prophet is not clever enough to see what's in store for himself. This is the most important idea of the fable.

   Ⓒ in the middle of the paragraph

   This answer is not correct because the middle of the paragraph tells about the robbery at the prophet's house and his reaction to the theft.

   Ⓓ by thinking about the most important idea in the paragraph

   This answer is not correct because the main idea is found in the last sentence.

★ Each paragraph in a reading passage has one main idea. The entire reading passage also has one main idea. The main idea of an entire reading passage is often found in the first or last paragraph.

★ The title of a reading passage often helps you identify the main idea.

Read this history report about a national symbol. Then answer the questions.

Who Is Uncle Sam?

Uncle Sam has been a symbol of the United States for more than 150 years. The first drawings of Uncle Sam appeared in the 1830s. For many years, his appearance took many forms. By the 1860s, drawings of Uncle Sam became more alike. Most pictures show a tall, thin man with a white beard. He is dressed in a waistcoat, striped pants, and a top hat with a band of stars.

Uncle Sam was actually based on a real person. He was a meat packer from Troy, New York. His name was Samuel Wilson, but everyone called him Uncle Sam. During the War of 1812, Wilson supplied meat to U.S. Army troops stationed near Troy. He stamped the letters *U.S.* on each wooden barrel of beef and pork. Soldiers thought the initials stood for *Uncle Sam*. The letters, however, were actually the abbreviation for the United States. Soon, *Uncle Sam* became the term for anything referring to the United States.

5. What is the main idea of the first paragraph?
   Ⓐ Uncle Sam has been a U.S. symbol for over 150 years.
   Ⓑ Uncle Sam is a tall, thin, bearded man.
   Ⓒ The first drawings of Uncle Sam appeared in the 1830s.
   Ⓓ For many years, Uncle Sam had different appearances.

6. What is the main idea of paragraph two?
   Ⓐ Uncle Sam was from Troy.
   Ⓑ Wilson sold meat to the U.S. Army.
   Ⓒ Uncle Sam was based on a real person.
   Ⓓ The letters *U.S.* stood for *Uncle Sam.*

7. What is the report mostly about?
   Ⓐ symbols of the United States
   Ⓑ one of our nation's oldest symbols
   Ⓒ what Uncle Sam looked like
   Ⓓ the real Uncle Sam

8. Which of these is another good title for the report?
   Ⓐ "Uncle Sam's Costume"
   Ⓑ "American Symbols"
   Ⓒ "Uncle Sam Wilson"
   Ⓓ "The History of Uncle Sam"

Read this article about a special kind of mouse. Then answer the questions.

In 1968, Douglas Engelbart demonstrated a new device at a computer conference. The gadget was a little wooden box on wheels. It was so small that it fit into the palm of the hand. Many people showed great interest in Engelbart's invention. It took 16 years, though, for "the mouse" to become a common computer tool.

In the late 1960s, computers were huge machines that cost millions of dollars. The first small computers began to appear during the 1970s, but few people used the early computers at home. Users needed to know special computer languages to operate them.

Personal computers became more popular after 1984. That year, Apple Computer, Inc. introduced the Macintosh™. The "Mac" was the first easy-to-use computer. Part of its basic equipment was a mouse. It controlled the movement of a pointer, or cursor, on the screen. The mouse allowed users to point and click to give commands to the computer. The mouse was also an excellent drawing tool. It could be used to form curved and straight lines.

Today, most computers come with a mouse. Some computers have other hand-controlled devices, too. Some of the newer devices are trackballs, touch pads, and joysticks.

9. What is the main idea of the first paragraph?
   Ⓐ Early personal computers were hard to operate.
   Ⓑ The Mac was the first easy-to-use computer.
   Ⓒ Douglas Engelbart invented the first computer mouse.
   Ⓓ A computer mouse is a hand-held device.

10. Paragraph three is mostly about
   Ⓐ how the Mac was made.
   Ⓑ how the Mac made good use of the mouse.
   Ⓒ how the mouse has changed in design.
   Ⓓ how to use different hand-held devices.

11. What is the article mostly about?
   Ⓐ a device that is as small as a mouse
   Ⓑ Macintosh computers
   Ⓒ an invention that changed the way computers were used
   Ⓓ the work of Douglas Engelbart

12. Which of these is the best title for the article?
   Ⓐ "How the Mouse Came to Be"
   Ⓑ "The Brave, Little Mouse"
   Ⓒ "A Man with a Vision"
   Ⓓ "Computer Tools"

★ A test question about the main idea may ask you what a reading passage is *mostly* or *mainly* about.

★ A test question about the main idea may ask you to choose the best title for a reading passage. A good title often identifies the main idea.

Here is a poem about someone's home. Read the poem. Then do Numbers 13 and 14.

Home Is Where the Heart Is
by stevan-adele Morley

Under a mighty mountain,
　　at the bottom of a hill,
The valley in the morning
　　is so beautiful and still.

Grandfather lives on the mountain;
　　my cousin lives on the hill,
But I live deep in the valley
　　and believe I always will.

Eagles nest on the mountain;
　　birds fly down from the hill,
Bringing songs to the valley
　　that echo through the chill.

When the snow melts on the mountain,
　　it comes streaming down the hill
To the river in the valley
　　that gives power to our mill.

There's folks who love the mountain,
　　and folks who love the hill,
But I live deep in the valley
　　and believe I always will.

Finding Main Idea

13. The poem is mostly about
    Ⓐ someone's feelings about living in the valley.
    Ⓑ people who like living on a mountain.
    Ⓒ a mill powered by melting snow.
    Ⓓ bird songs that echo through a valley.

Finding Main Idea

14. Another good title for the poem is
    Ⓐ "Songs from Up High."
    Ⓑ "A Mighty Mountain."
    Ⓒ "My Valley Home."
    Ⓓ "Mountain Folk."

Here is a folktale from the Kutchin Indians of Canada. Read the folktale. Then do Numbers 15 and 16.

In the beginning, Bear had the moon. It was a big round ball that looked like seal fat. Many of the animals wanted there to be moonlight, but Bear preferred the darkness, so he kept the moon tied up in a bag by his bed.

Fox was anxious to have moonlight, and he decided to steal the moon from Bear. He went to get help from Raven, who was Bear's uncle. Raven also wished for moonlight, and he agreed to assist Fox. Together, they went one evening to Bear's camp to carry out their plan.

After they had been welcomed by Bear, Raven began to entertain them by telling stories. Soon Bear became drowsy, but Raven still continued telling story after story. Bear could not control his sleepiness, and kept dropping off for a nap. But every time he came awake, there was Raven still droning on. Finally, Bear fell asleep.

During all this time, Fox had been looking for the place where Bear had hidden the moon. Then he saw the bag tied up near the bed, and as soon as Bear was asleep, Fox seized the bag. Quickly opening it, he ran outside with the moon and hurled it into the sky.

Bear awoke just in time to see the moon go sailing off into space. He immediately called out, "Stop, moon. Let there be no moonlight."

But Fox, too, called out, "Sail on, moon. Let there be plenty of moonlight."

That is why every month some of the nights have moonlight while the others do not.

Finding Main Idea

15. The folktale is mostly about
- Ⓐ why Bear preferred darkness.
- Ⓑ how the moon was taken away from Bear.
- Ⓒ when the moon appears in the sky.
- Ⓓ who is responsible for the moonlight.

Finding Main Idea

16. Which of these is the best title for the folktale?
- Ⓐ "A Moon for Bear"
- Ⓑ "Sail On, Moon"
- Ⓒ "Raven, the Storyteller"
- Ⓓ "Fox and Raven Steal the Moon"

STRATEGY 2

PART ONE: LEARN ABOUT FACTS AND DETAILS

Read this paragraph about a famous building. The main idea is found in the last sentence and is underlined for you. As you read, think about the sentences that tell more about the main idea.

The Taj Mahal is named for Mumtaz Mahal. She was the wife of Indian ruler Shah Jahan. When his beloved wife died, Shah Jahan ordered that a great tomb be built in her memory. Work began on the Taj Mahal in 1632. It took 20,000 workers more than 20 years to complete. The huge, white marble tomb is surrounded by gardens and fountains. A long reflecting pool is set in front of it. <u>The Taj Mahal is India's most famous monument.</u>

The sentences that tell more about the main idea are

The Taj Mahal is named for Mumtaz Mahal.

She was the wife of Indian ruler Shah Jahan.

When his beloved wife died, Shah Jahan ordered that a great tomb be built in her memory.

Work began on the Taj Mahal in 1632.

It took 20,000 workers more than 20 years to complete.

The huge, white marble tomb is surrounded by gardens and fountains.

A long reflecting pool is set in front of it.

Sentences that tell more about the main idea are called **facts and details**. Facts and details explain or support the most important idea in the paragraph.

★ Facts and details provide information about the main idea.

★ Facts and details often tell about the *who, what, where, when, why,* and *how* of the main idea.

Read this paragraph about the planets. The main idea is found in the first sentence and is underlined for you. As you read, think about the facts and details that tell more about the main idea. Then answer the questions.

Orbiting the Planets

<u>Some of the planets in our solar system have more moons than others.</u> Mercury and Venus, the planets closest to the sun, have no moons. Our planet, Earth, has one moon. Pluto, the most distant and smallest planet, also has one moon. Two oddly shaped moons orbit our neighbor Mars. Several planets, though, have many moons. Eight moons revolve around blue Neptune. At least 15 moons orbit Uranus, and at least 16 orbit Jupiter, the largest planet. Saturn, the planet with the largest and most spectacular rings, has the most moons. Scientists have confirmed that at least 18 moons orbit Saturn.

1. Which planet has the most moons?
   Ⓐ Jupiter
   Ⓑ Uranus
   Ⓒ Saturn
   Ⓓ Neptune

2. Which detail tells something about Pluto?
   Ⓐ It has at least 15 moons.
   Ⓑ It is closest to the sun.
   Ⓒ Eight moons revolve around it.
   Ⓓ It is the most distant and smallest planet.

Work with a partner. Talk about your answers to questions 1 and 2. Tell why you chose the answers you did.

Remember: Facts and details explain or support the main idea.

★ Look for sentences that provide information about the main idea.

★ Look for sentences that tell about the *who, what, where, when, why,* and *how* of the main idea.

Read this fairy tale by Hans Christian Andersen. As you read, ask yourself, "What is the main idea? What facts and details tell *more* about the main idea?" Then answer the questions.

The Princess and the Pea

There once was a prince who wanted to marry a princess, but she would have to be a *real* princess. The prince traveled all around the world to find his princess. There were princesses enough, but there was always something about them that was not quite right. So, the disappointed prince went home.

One evening, a terrible storm erupted. Thunder boomed and lightning flashed, and the rain poured down in torrents. Suddenly, there was a knocking at the city gate. The king himself went to open it and found a princess standing outside. What a sight she was after all that rain. Water streamed from her hair and clothes. Despite her sloppy appearance, she claimed that she was a real princess.

"Yes, we will soon find that out," thought the doubtful queen. But she said nothing and went into the bedchamber, took all the bedding off the bedstead, and laid a pea at the bottom. Then she took 40 eiderdown mattresses and laid them upon the pea. On this the princess had to lie all night.

In the morning, the princess was asked how she had slept. "Oh, miserably!" she said. "Goodness knows what was in my bed, but I was lying on something hard, and now I am black and blue all over."

Now it was clear that the young woman was a real princess, because she had felt the pea through all those mattresses. Nobody but a true princess could be so delicate. So, the prince and the princess married, and the pea was put in a museum, where it may still be today.

3. Who put the pea under the mattresses?
   - Ⓐ the king
   - Ⓑ the queen
   - Ⓒ the prince
   - Ⓓ the princess

4. How did the prince feel when he went home without having found a real princess?
   - Ⓐ puzzled
   - Ⓒ disappointed
   - Ⓑ angry
   - Ⓓ doubtful

Look at the answer choices for each question. Read why each answer choice is correct or not correct.

3. Who put the pea under the mattresses?

Ⓐ the king

This answer is not correct because the only time the king is mentioned in the fairy tale is when he greets the princess at the city gate.

● the queen

This answer is correct because paragraph three states that the queen laid 40 mattresses upon the pea.

Ⓒ the prince

This answer is not correct because the fairy tale never mentions that the prince was involved in placing the pea under the mattresses.

Ⓓ the princess

This answer is not correct because the fairy tale indicates that the princess knew nothing about the pea being put under the mattresses she would sleep upon. When she awoke the next morning, she had no idea why she had slept so badly.

4. How did the prince feel when he went home without having found a real princess?

Ⓐ puzzled

This answer is not correct because the word puzzled *was not used in the fairy tale to describe the prince.*

Ⓑ angry

This answer is not correct because the fairy tale never states that the prince was angry about anything.

● disappointed

This answer is correct because the first paragraph states that, after he failed to find a real princess, "the disappointed prince went home."

Ⓓ doubtful

This answer is not correct because it was the queen who was doubtful, not the prince. She doubted that the princess who appeared at the gate was a real princess.

Facts and details give additional meaning to the main idea of a reading passage.
When you read, look for sentences that

★ describe a person, place, or thing.

★ tell the order in which things happen.

★ explain how to do something.

★ share an experience, idea, or opinion.

Read this message from the back of a postcard. Then answer the questions.

Dear Freddie,

Here I am in the Philippines, at last. I haven't done much yet. However, I did see some unusual sights on the drive from the airport to my uncle's home. I spotted these buses called "jeepneys." The owners paint their jeepneys in bold, bright colors. Then they cover them in all kinds of decorations. Jeepneys also have many mirrors—more than are needed for safety!

My taxi driver told me that the first jeepneys were created from U.S. Army jeeps. The jeeps had been left on the Philippine Islands after World War II. Filipinos made the vehicles longer to hold more passengers. Today, most jeepneys can carry about 17 people comfortably. But many more passengers usually squeeze in.

Your friend,
Eric

5. What are jeepneys?
   Ⓐ taxis
   Ⓑ U.S. Army tanks
   Ⓒ buses
   Ⓓ cars made in the Philippines

6. Which of these is a fact about jeepneys?
   Ⓐ The first jeepneys were made during World War II.
   Ⓑ The U.S. Army created the first jeepneys.
   Ⓒ Jeepneys are noisy.
   Ⓓ Jeepneys are brightly painted.

7. Where did Eric first see jeepneys?
   Ⓐ on his uncle's street
   Ⓑ on the drive to his uncle's home
   Ⓒ on a U.S. Army base
   Ⓓ on a bus tour

8. Which detail tells more about the main idea of paragraph two?
   Ⓐ Owners like to decorate their jeepneys.
   Ⓑ Army jeeps were left on the Philippines after World War I.
   Ⓒ Jeepneys are longer than army jeeps.
   Ⓓ Only 17 people can fit in a jeepney.

Read this article about a favorite sport. Then answer the questions.

Today, soccer is the world's most popular sport. Millions of children and adults play the sport. Pelé, who is probably the sport's greatest player, once called soccer "the beautiful game."

Soccer is played on a field that is between 100 and 130 yards long and 50 and 100 yards wide. A goal net eight yards wide and eight feet high sits at each end of the field. Each team has 11 players—ten field players and one goalkeeper. The object of the game is to move a leather-covered rubber ball down the field by dribbling or passing. When the ball is near the opposing team's goal, players try to shoot it into the net. Players may use their feet, knees, elbows, chest, and head to control the ball. Only the goalkeepers may touch the ball with their hands. Each game is divided into halves. The team that scores more goals by the end of the second half wins the game.

Since 1900, soccer teams from various nations have competed in the Summer Olympics, which are held every four years. The true soccer championship, however, is the World Cup soccer tournament. It is also held every four years. More than one billion people worldwide watch the World Cup games.

9. What is one detail that tells about soccer?
   Ⓐ Goal nets are eight feet wide and eight feet high.
   Ⓑ Soccer was first played in 1800.
   Ⓒ Only goalkeepers can touch the ball with their hands.
   Ⓓ Over one billion people play on soccer teams around the world.

10. What detail tells about the main idea of paragraph two?
    Ⓐ Players may use their feet to control the ball.
    Ⓑ A soccer team has 10 players.
    Ⓒ The World Cup is held every four years.
    Ⓓ Millions of people play soccer.

11. Who is Pelé?
    Ⓐ a popular soccer coach
    Ⓑ an Olympic athlete
    Ⓒ a goalkeeper
    Ⓓ a famous soccer player

12. Which of these tells more about the main idea of the last paragraph?
    Ⓐ National soccer teams compete in the Winter Olympics.
    Ⓑ The true soccer championship is the World Cup soccer tournament.
    Ⓒ Billions of fans attend the World Cup games.
    Ⓓ Soccer games are divided into halves.

★ A test question about facts and details may ask you about something that is stated in a reading passage.

★ A test question about facts and details may ask you about the *who, what, where, when, why,* and *how* of the main idea.

Here is an essay that a student wrote after a trip to the zoo. Read the essay. Then do Numbers 13 and 14.

A Walking Pine Cone

Have you ever heard of a pangolin? Before this weekend, I would have guessed that a pangolin was some type of musical instrument. During a visit to the zoo, though, I learned that a pangolin is actually a kind of anteater. I thought it was one of the most interesting animals in the zoo. Certainly, it was one of the most unusual looking.

The pangolin normally lives in Africa and India. The pangolin looks like a giant pine cone with legs. Its body is about three-to-five feet long and covered with large brown scales. The scales are thick and sharp to protect the anteater. The pangolin can also roll up into a tight ball for safety. Once the pangolin is curled up, it's impossible for its enemies to unroll it!

Although its nose is not quite as long as the nose of other anteaters, the pangolin does have a good sense of smell. It uses this sense to find food at night. Pangolins eat mostly ants and termites. The anteaters use the sharp claws on their front limbs to rip open the insects' nests. Then they use their long, sticky tongue to pick up the bugs they find inside. Pangolins don't have teeth for chewing their food, so they swallow small pebbles to help them crush up any insects in their stomach.

Most pangolins climb trees. They wrap their long, strong tail around branches to hold on. On the ground, they walk on short hind legs with their long tail stretched out behind for balance.

Recalling Facts and Details

13. What is one fact about pangolins?
   Ⓐ They live in Africa only.
   Ⓑ They have a short nose.
   Ⓒ Thick, sharp scales cover their bodies.
   Ⓓ They roll up into a tight ball to sleep.

Recalling Facts and Details

14. Which part of their body do pangolins use to pick up insects?
   Ⓐ nose
   Ⓑ tongue
   Ⓒ front claws
   Ⓓ teeth

Here is a medieval tale from England. Read the tale. Then do Numbers 15 and 16.

The Boy Merlin

Long ago, a wicked king named Vortigern ruled most of England. Vortigern had many enemies, and eventually he was driven into the mountains of Wales. There, Vortigern tried to build a stone fortress that would protect him from attack. Each day, the king's workers raised the fortress walls, but each night, the rocks tumbled down. Finally, the king called in his wizards to explain the mystery.

"You must find a child born without a human father," they advised. "Slay him, and then the fortress walls will stand firm." So, the king sent out a search party to find such a child.

One day, the king's men came upon several children playing ball. One boy threw the ball again and again, but none of the others could catch it. Suddenly, another child shouted out, "You never play fairly, Merlin! You're just a trickster who never had a father!"

The king's men began asking the villagers about the boy. Upon learning that the child's father was not a mortal man, the king's men seized Merlin. Then they rode back to Wales, where Merlin was brought before the king.

"Why have you sent for me?" the young boy demanded. When Vortigern told him the reason, Merlin said, "Your wizards are wrong. By slaying me, you won't keep your fortress standing. There is a pool of water beneath the fortress that is making the ground unsteady. Have your workers dig into the earth until they find the pool. Order them to drain the pool. At the bottom, they will find two stones. Inside the stones are two sleeping dragons."

The king instructed his workers to do as Merlin said. They uncovered the stones, from which two great dragons, one white and one red, burst forth. The dragons began to fight fiercely. At last, the white dragon killed the red one.

"What is the meaning of the dragons' fight?" the frightened king asked.

"The white dragon stands for enemies who will someday slay you," Merlin calmly explained.

Soon afterward, King Vortigern was, indeed, killed by his foes.

Recalling Facts and Details

15. What material was used to build Vortigern's fortress?
  Ⓐ stones
  Ⓑ wood
  Ⓒ mud
  Ⓓ iron

Recalling Facts and Details

16. Which of these is a fact from the tale?
  Ⓐ Merlin became one of the king's wizards.
  Ⓑ Merlin told the king that his wizards were wrong.
  Ⓒ Two red dragons lived under the king's fortress.
  Ⓓ Earthquakes caused the fortress walls to tumble down each night.

STRATEGY 3

PART ONE: LEARN ABOUT SEQUENCE

Read this article that describes an art project. As you read, think about the order of the steps that are followed to complete the project.

Making a Collage

The art teacher, Ms. Shurtleff, was explaining a new project to her fifth-grade students. "We'll be making a design out of pasted pictures or scraps of paper or fabric," she said. "It's called a collage."

"First," Ms. Shurtleff instructed, "think of a theme for your collage. Second, gather your materials. You'll need scissors, glue, and poster board for the background. You'll also need magazines, colored paper or tissue, and scraps of cloth. You can also use small objects such as buttons and shells."

"Third," she continued, "cut out pictures and words from magazines to develop your theme. Next, add materials that will give your collage color, shape, and texture. Then move the pieces around on the poster board until you have the design you want. Last, glue the pieces to the poster board to create your collage."

The order of the steps that are followed to complete the collage is

First, think of a theme for your collage.

Second, gather your materials.

Third, cut out pictures and words from magazines to develop your theme.

Next, add materials that will give your collage color, shape, and texture.

Then move the pieces around until you have the design you want.

Last, glue the pieces to the poster board to create your collage.

The order in which things are done or events happen is called **sequence**. The steps for completing a set of directions often follow a sequence.

★ Clue words such as *first, next, then, last, finally, before,* and *after* often tell you when things are done or events happen.

★ Clues such as the time of day, the day of the week, the month, the season, and the year tell when things happen.

★ In a story without clue words, think about the beginning, the middle, and the ending to help you figure out sequence. In an article without clue words, think about the order in which things happen or how things are done.

Read this story about a clever trick. As you read, think about what happens first, second, and so on. Then answer the questions.

The Mind Reader

Abe told his friend Corey that he could read minds and was ready to prove his power as a mind reader. First, Abe spread out nine magazines on the floor. He then arranged the magazines in three rows of three magazines each.

Abe's sister Sandra, who knew how to do the trick, acted as his assistant. She placed a blindfold over Abe's eyes. Next, she turned him around so that his back faced Corey. Abe then asked his friend to touch one of the magazines.

After Corey made his choice, Abe turned around and removed his blindfold. He told Corey to concentrate on the correct magazine, but not to look directly at it.

With a measuring stick, Sandra pointed to the bottom right corner of the first magazine in the top row. "Is it this one?" she asked Abe.

Abe answered, "No." Sandra continued to point to magazines, from the top row to the bottom row. Each time, she asked, "Is this the one?" Each time, Abe shook his head "No." Finally, when the pointer touched the last magazine in the bottom row, Abe nodded his head and said, "Yes, that's the one."

Corey was astounded. He wondered how Abe had figured out that the correct magazine was at the bottom right. Can you guess Abe's secret?

---

1. What did Abe do first?
   Ⓐ He put on a blindfold.
   Ⓑ He placed nine magazines on the floor.
   Ⓒ He asked Corey to touch a magazine.
   Ⓓ He nodded his head.

2. Which clue word tells what Abe did last?
   Ⓐ first
   Ⓑ then
   Ⓒ next
   Ⓓ finally

 Work with a partner. Talk about your answers to questions 1 and 2. Tell why you chose the answers you did.

Remember: Sequence tells the order in which things are done or events happen.

★ Look for clue words such as *first, next, then, last, finally, before,* and *after.*
These clue words help you figure out the order in which things are done or
events happen in a reading passage.

★ Look for clues that tell about the time of day, the day of the week, the month,
the season, and the year.

★ When there are no clue words in a story, think about the beginning, the middle,
and the ending to help you understand the sequence. When there are no clue words
in an article, think about the order in which things happen or how things are done.

**Read this article about a great wonder. As you read, think about the clue words
that tell you the order in which things happened. Then answer the questions.**

The Great Wall of China

About two thousand years ago, China's first emperor
ordered the building of a huge wall along his empire's
northern borders. After the wall was built, it was used
to protect the Chinese from enemies in the north.

Over a million people worked on the project.
The wall took more than ten years to build and
eventually covered 2,150 miles. First, the builders
piled dirt as high as 39 feet. Then they pounded the
dirt into hard mounds. Each mound was about 32 feet
thick. Next, the workers shaped the huge mounds
with bamboo poles. Last, they fitted stones and clay
bricks over the sides and the top. The top became
a road that was wide enough for six soldiers on
horseback to ride side by side.

Today, the Great Wall of China is still the biggest structure ever built. It's the only human-
made object you'd be able to see if you looked back at Earth from the moon.

3. What did the builders of the Great Wall
of China do first?
   Ⓐ They pounded dirt into hard mounds.
   Ⓑ They created high piles of dirt.
   Ⓒ They fitted stones and bricks over
   the sides and top of the mounds.
   Ⓓ They shaped the mounds with
   bamboo poles.

4. Which clue word tells what the workers
did second?
   Ⓐ then
   Ⓑ next
   Ⓒ after
   Ⓓ last

Look at the answer choices for each question. Read why each answer choice is correct or not correct.

3. What did the builders of the Great Wall of China do first?

Ⓐ They pounded dirt into hard mounds.

This answer is not correct because the builders created high piles of dirt before they pounded the dirt into hard mounds.

● They created high piles of dirt.

This answer is correct because paragraph two states "First, the builders piled dirt as high as 39 feet."

Ⓒ They fitted stones and bricks over the sides and top of the mounds.

This answer is not correct because paragraph two states that the builders did this step last.

Ⓓ They shaped the mounds with bamboo poles.

This answer is not correct because the builders had to pile the dirt and pound it into mounds before they could shape the mounds with bamboo poles.

4. Which clue word tells what the workers did second?

● then

This answer is correct because this clue tells what happened immediately after the workers created high piles of dirt, which was the first step. Pounding the dirt into hard mounds must be what the workers did second.

Ⓑ next

This answer is not correct because the word next is used in the article to describe what happened after the dirt was piled high and pounded into hard mounds. Shaping the mounds with bamboo poles must then be the third step.

Ⓒ after

This answer is not correct because the word after is used to describe what happened once the Great Wall was built.

Ⓓ last

This answer is not correct because the word last is used to describe the final step of construction of the Great Wall.

★ If a reading passage does not contain clue words, ask yourself questions such as "What happened first?" and "What happened next?" to help figure out the order of events in a reading passage.

★ Stories are usually told in the order in which the events occurred—from the beginning to the ending. Not all stories are told entirely in time order; sometimes, a past event is introduced in the beginning or middle of a story.

Read this riddle and its solution. Then answer the questions.

One day, a farmer had to carry a goat, a wolf, and a cabbage across a river. The farmer, however, could bring only one item across the river at a time. He knew that if he left the goat, the wolf, and the cabbage alone, the goat would eat the cabbage, and the wolf would eat the goat. It took the farmer a long time to figure out a solution to his problem. At last, he realized how he could get himself and the goat, the wolf, and the cabbage safely across.

First, the farmer rowed across the river with the goat and left the animal alone on the opposite side. Second, he rowed back, picked up the wolf, and brought it across. However, he did not leave the wolf with the goat. The goat returned with him in the rowboat. Next, the farmer dropped off the goat and made another trip across the river with the cabbage only. He left the wolf with the cabbage and then went back to get the goat. After the farmer and the goat crossed the river again, they joined the wolf and cabbage.

5. Which of these did the farmer do first?
   Ⓐ He rowed across the river with the goat.
   Ⓑ He brought the wolf across.
   Ⓒ He left the goat alone.
   Ⓓ He brought the cabbage across.

6. What happened after the wolf was brought across the river?
   Ⓐ The wolf ate the goat.
   Ⓑ The farmer rowed back with the goat.
   Ⓒ The wolf joined the cabbage.
   Ⓓ The farmer went back to get the goat.

7. Which clue word tells what the farmer did last?
   Ⓐ last   Ⓒ after
   Ⓑ next   Ⓓ finally

8. Before he tried to cross the river, the farmer
   Ⓐ bought a rowboat.
   Ⓑ separated the wolf and the goat.
   Ⓒ worried a lot.
   Ⓓ thought of a way to bring the goat, the wolf, and the cabbage across safely.

Read this biography of a courageous woman. Then answer the questions.

A Fearless Conductor

Harriet Tubman helped free more than 300 slaves. She led so many slaves to freedom that she became known as the "Moses of Her People."

Harriet was born on a Maryland plantation about 1821. She was one of 11 children born to the slaves Harriet and Benjamin Ross. When the slave child was just six years old, she began working as a maid and a cook. At age 12, she went to work in the fields.

In 1844, the young field hand married a freed black man named John Tubman. Five years later, Harriet Tubman heard rumors that she was about to be sold farther south, so she ran away. She traveled north on the Underground Railroad. The Underground Railroad was a network of safe hiding places leading all the way to Canada.

Tubman made it safely to Philadelphia. Once she was free, she grew determined to help other slaves escape. She became one of the leading conductors of the railroad. From 1850 to 1860, she made 19 trips back into the South.

Helping runaway slaves was against the law. Slave owners offered huge rewards for Tubman's capture. Tubman, though, was never caught, nor were any of her runaways. She later said, "I never ran my train off the track, and I never lost a passenger."

9. In the biography, clues that tell about the sequence are
   Ⓐ months.
   Ⓑ days of the week.
   Ⓒ times of day.
   Ⓓ years.

10. What happened in Harriet Tubman's life during the year 1844?
   Ⓐ She became a field hand.
   Ⓑ She got married.
   Ⓒ She fled to Philadelphia.
   Ⓓ She led slaves to freedom.

11. When did Harriet Tubman run away?
   Ⓐ 1821
   Ⓑ 1844
   Ⓒ 1849
   Ⓓ 1850

12. In 1860, Harriet Tubman
   Ⓐ became a railroad conductor.
   Ⓑ made her last trip back into the South.
   Ⓒ was captured.
   Ⓓ made it safely to Philadelphia.

★ A test question about sequence may ask you when certain things happened in a reading passage.

★ A test question about sequence may ask you to put events from a reading passage in order.

★ A test question about sequence may contain words such as *first*, *second*, *last*, *before*, or *after*.

Here is a folktale from China. Read the folktale. Then do Numbers 13 and 14.

One day, three blind men were talking about this and that when one said, "I have heard about an animal called an elephant. I wish that I could touch it to learn what it is like."

"Yes," exclaimed the second blind man. "I would also like to touch an elephant."

"Me, too," the third blind man said enthusiastically.

A man who owned an elephant just happened to pass by and overheard the three men's conversation. "I have an elephant," the owner said. "I will lead you to it."

The three blind men went with the man and soon came to a spot where an elephant was standing. The owner said, "Here is my elephant. You may take turns touching it."

The owner brought the first blind man to the elephant. The man reached out with his hands and ran them up and down the elephant's leg. "Now I understand," he said.

Then the second blind man took a turn. He was by the rear of the elephant, so when he reached out, his hands grasped the tail. "I know now," said the man.

When it was the third blind man's turn, his hands stroked the elephant's trunk. The trunk moved up and down, nearly lifting the man off the ground. "Oh," he said, "I get it."

The three men thanked the owner. As they walked back, the second blind man said, "I had heard that an elephant is strong, but in my opinion, it must be very weak. Why, when I held the creature between my hands, it was not much bigger than a rope."

"You are mistaken, my friend," said the third blind man. "An elephant is strong, very strong. It is as big and long as a giant, powerful snake."

"You are both wrong," said the first blind man. "An elephant is like a thick tree trunk."

The men began to argue. And they may be arguing still. Each man was partly right, of course, but they were all wrong.

Understanding Sequence

13. After the three blind men touched the elephant, they
    Ⓐ followed the owner.
    Ⓑ thanked the owner.
    Ⓒ argued with the owner.
    Ⓓ walked back to the owner.

Understanding Sequence

14. The boxes tell about some of the events in the folktale.

An elephant owner led three blind men to his elephant.		One man grasped the elephant's tail.
1	2	3

Which of these belongs in box 2?
    Ⓐ One man touched the elephant's leg.
    Ⓑ The three men talked about this and that.
    Ⓒ The elephant's trunk moved up and down.
    Ⓓ The three men began to argue.

Here is an article from a food magazine. Read the article.
Then do Numbers 15 and 16.

Fast Foods for Fast Lives

Who first put ground beef between slices of bread? No one knows for sure, but the hamburger sandwich first became popular about 100 years ago. Factory workers especially liked this hand-held meal. They didn't have much time or money. They could buy two hamburgers for one nickel at traveling lunch carts. By the turn of the century, dining cars, called "diners," replaced the carts.

In 1916, J. Walter Anderson of Wichita, Kansas, invented the hamburger bun. Five years later, Anderson and a partner built a restaurant shaped like a castle and painted it white. White Castle grew to become the first hamburger chain.

Soon after White Castle was born, the first drive-in restaurants appeared. These roadside stands used carhops to serve people in their cars. The drive-ins also had fun shapes and bright signs to draw in customers off the road.

In 1948, the McDonald brothers of California introduced a new kind of hamburger place. There were no waiters at their new restaurant. Customers ordered their meals at a walk-up window. McDonald's could offer quick service because the food was sent to the restaurant ready to cook. The hamburgers were already shaped into patties. The french fries were cut and ready to be dipped in hot oil. Other restaurants sold their hamburgers for 35 cents. McDonald's hamburgers, though, were only 15 cents. French fries were a dime.

Dozens of businesses soon copied the idea of selling quick burgers at low prices. Today fast-food places are everywhere: on roadways, in town centers, in shopping malls, in airports, and even in school lunchrooms.

Understanding Sequence

15. What appeared after drive-in restaurants?
    - Ⓐ White Castle restaurants
    - Ⓑ McDonald's restaurants
    - Ⓒ dining cars
    - Ⓓ traveling lunch carts

Understanding Sequence

16. Before McDonald's opened,
    - Ⓐ french fries didn't exist.
    - Ⓑ restaurants weren't built on roadways.
    - Ⓒ there were no hamburger chains.
    - Ⓓ restaurant service took longer.

REVIEW STRATEGIES 1–3

PART ONE: READ AN ARTICLE

Here is an article about Vietnam's early history. Read the article.
Then do Numbers 1 through 6.

Two thousand years ago, the Chinese ruled the land that is now Vietnam. Many Vietnamese wanted freedom from Chinese rule. This dream burned strongly in the heart and mind of Trung Trac, the wife of a Vietnamese noble named Thi Sach.

In A.D. 29, a new Chinese governor took control in Vietnam. His name was Su Ting, and he was greedy and cruel. Trung Trac urged her husband to challenge the Chinese ruler. Thi Sach started to stir up trouble. Su Ting reacted by having Thi Sach put to death. The murder led Trung Trac and her younger sister, Trung Nhi, to raise an army of Vietnamese nobles and peasants. In A.D. 39, the Trung sisters led the troops in battle against the Chinese.

By A.D. 40, the Vietnamese had driven Su Ting out of the country. The Vietnamese kingdom was set up, and Trung Trac was declared queen. The new kingdom, though, did not last long. Within two years, the Chinese had sent the great general Ma Yuan into Vietnam with more than 20,000 soldiers.

Many Vietnamese felt they had no chance against such a large army. Because Trung Trac grew afraid that her followers would abandon her, she ordered an immediate attack. The Chinese easily defeated her small army. Several thousand Vietnamese soldiers were captured and put to death.

Trung Trac and her most loyal supporters retreated into the mountains. According to one story, Ma Yuan captured the Trung sisters and had them

killed. Another story says that the sisters died from disease. Still a third tale says that they disappeared into the clouds. The most popular belief is that the Trung sisters drowned themselves in a river rather than face the shame of surrender.

The Chinese controlled Vietnam for more than a thousand years altogether. Finally, in A.D. 939, General Ngo Quyen led the Vietnamese in a successful revolt against the Chinese.

Finding Main Idea

1. What is the article mostly about?
   Ⓐ the rule of Su Ting
   Ⓑ the Trung sisters' fight for Vietnam's freedom
   Ⓒ the mystery of the Trung sisters' death
   Ⓓ cruel Chinese rulers

Recalling Facts and Details

4. Who led the Vietnamese in a successful revolt against the Chinese?
   Ⓐ Trung Nhi
   Ⓑ Thi Sach
   Ⓒ Ngo Quyen
   Ⓓ Ma Yuon

Finding Main Idea

2. What would be a good title for this article?
   Ⓐ "The Legend of the Trung Sisters"
   Ⓑ "General Ma Yuan"
   Ⓒ "The Death of Thi Sach"
   Ⓓ "Queen Trung Trac"

Understanding Sequence

5. Which of these happened last?
   Ⓐ The Trung sisters raised an army.
   Ⓑ The Vietnamese drove out Su Ting.
   Ⓒ Su Ting took control of Vietnam.
   Ⓓ Thi Sach stirred up trouble.

Recalling Facts and Details

3. Su Ting ruled Vietnam from
   Ⓐ A.D. 39 to A.D. 40.
   Ⓑ A.D. 929 to A.D. 939.
   Ⓒ A.D. 29 to A.D. 39.
   Ⓓ A.D. 29 to A.D. 40.

Understanding Sequence

6. After the Chinese defeated the Vietnamese army,
   Ⓐ Su Ting regained control of Vietnam.
   Ⓑ Trung Trac ordered an immediate attack.
   Ⓒ Trung Trac retreated into the mountains.
   Ⓓ Trung Trac was declared queen.

Here is a German fairy tale by the Brothers Grimm. Read the fairy tale. Then do Numbers 7 through 12.

Rumpelstiltskin

One day, a poor miller met the king. Wanting to impress the king, the miller said, "I have a daughter who can spin straw into gold." The king told the miller to bring the girl to his castle.

When the girl arrived, the king led her into a room full of straw. He gave her a spinning wheel and said, "If you value your life, you will spin all this straw into gold by morning." Then he left her alone and locked the door.

The poor girl had no notion of how to spin gold out of straw. Her distress grew so great that she began to weep. Suddenly, the door opened, and in came a strange little man. "What will you give me if I spin this straw for you?" he asked.

"My necklace," said the girl. The little man took the necklace and then spun all the straw into gold. When the king came at sunrise and saw the glittering gold, he took the girl into a larger room filled with straw and asked her to do the same. Again, the little man came. This time, the girl gave him her ring in exchange for his help. The next morning, the king was delighted. He then took the girl to an even bigger room full of straw. "If you spin all this straw into gold," the king told her, "I will make you my wife."

The little man appeared for the third time. "I will spin this straw into gold," he said, "but you must give me your firstborn child when you are queen." The girl agreed, and soon she became queen.

A year later, the queen had a baby, and soon after, the little man appeared to claim the child. The queen offered him all the riches of the kingdom if she could keep her child.

But the little man said, "I'd rather have a living child than all the gold and jewels in the world."

When she heard this, the queen began to weep so bitterly that the little man took pity on her. "Very well," he said, "I will give you three days. If you can guess my name within that time, you may keep your child."

The queen struggled to think of unusual names. She also sent a messenger to search for new names. On the third day, the messenger returned with a story about a little man in the forest who had hopped around a fire on one foot and sung, "Today I brew, tomorrow I bake. And after that the child I'll take. I'm the winner of the game. Rumpelstiltskin is my name."

Not long afterward, the little man appeared before the queen. "Well, Your Majesty," he said, "what is my name?"

And the queen said, "By any chance, is your name Rumpelstiltskin?"

At that, the little man got so angry that he stomped off and never came back.

Finding Main Idea

7. The main idea of the fairy tale is found
   - Ⓐ in the first paragraph.
   - Ⓑ in the middle of the story.
   - Ⓒ in the last paragraph.
   - Ⓓ by thinking about the most important idea in the story.

Finding Main Idea

8. Which of these is another good title for the fairy tale?
   - Ⓐ "A Greedy King"
   - Ⓑ "A Little Man with a Strange Name"
   - Ⓒ "The Miller's Clever Daughter"
   - Ⓓ "Straw and Gold"

Recalling Facts and Details

9. Who first discovered the little man's name?
   - Ⓐ the king
   - Ⓑ the queen
   - Ⓒ the messenger
   - Ⓓ the miller

Recalling Facts and Details

10. Which detail tells that the king was mean?
    - Ⓐ He told the girl that if she valued her life, she must spin the straw into gold.
    - Ⓑ He told the miller to bring his daughter to the castle.
    - Ⓒ He was delighted to see all the gold.
    - Ⓓ He took the girl's jewelry.

Understanding Sequence

11. What did the girl give the little man the second time he came to help her?
    - Ⓐ her necklace
    - Ⓑ her ring
    - Ⓒ her gold
    - Ⓓ her child

Understanding Sequence

12. The boxes tell about some things that happened in the story.

	The king told the girl to spin all the straw into gold by morning.	A little man asked the girl what she would give him to spin the straw.
1	2	3

Which of these belongs in box 1?
    - Ⓐ The king left the girl alone and locked the door.
    - Ⓑ A little man came in the room.
    - Ⓒ The miller's daughter began to weep.
    - Ⓓ The girl arrived at the castle.

STRATEGY 4

PART ONE: LEARN ABOUT CAUSE AND EFFECT

Read this paragraph about a group of people who once lived in the Caribbean. As you read, think about one thing that happened to these people and why.

The Taíno once lived on the islands in the northern Caribbean. They were the first people to welcome Christopher Columbus when he arrived in the New World in 1492. The Taíno thought that Columbus and his crew were gods. They gave their visitors many gifts. The Spanish, though, treated the Taíno badly. First, they claimed all the Taíno land. Then they forced the islanders to dig for gold in barren mines. As a result, many Taíno died from overwork. Others starved. Diseases, which the Spanish brought to the islands, were the main reason, however, that most Taíno died. By 1530, the Taíno population had almost completely disappeared.

One thing that happened to the Taíno and why is

What happened: **By 1530, the Taíno population had almost completely disappeared.**
Why it happened: **The Spanish brought diseases to the islands.**

What happens and why is called **cause and effect**.
Why something happens is the **cause**. *The Spanish brought diseases to the islands.*
What happens because of the cause is the **effect**. *By 1530, the Taíno population had almost completely disappeared.*

★ A cause is the reason that something happens.

★ An effect is the result, or what happens because of the cause.

★ Clue words such as *so, so that, since, because,* and *if* often signal cause and effect. Other clues words are *reason* and *as a result.*

Read these instructions for an art project. As you read, look for clue words to help you understand what happens and why it happens. Then answer the questions.

T-shirt Art

Here's a great craft idea for a party. Have your guests design their own T-shirts! You'll need plain white T-shirts, a set of fabric crayons, blank paper, pencils, and straight pins. Since you'll also be using a hot iron, be sure to ask an adult to help.

First, sketch a design on a sheet of paper. Be sure to draw any letters backward, because the final design will be a mirror image of what you sketch. Second, color the design with the fabric crayons. Press down hard so that a thick coat of wax appears on the paper. Third, slide a sheet of paper inside the T-shirt so that the back of the shirt is protected. Then pin the finished design, crayon-side down, onto the front of the shirt. Secure the paper tightly so that the design won't shift or smudge. Next, turn on the iron. When the iron is hot, move it back and forth over the sheet of paper. To check whether the design is transferring properly, carefully unpin one corner of the paper. If the colors aren't dark enough, for example, carefully replace the paper and iron some more. If your guests follow these steps correctly, everyone should go home with a wearable souvenir.

1. A sheet of paper is slid inside the T-shirt so that
   Ⓐ the design doesn't shift or smudge.
   Ⓑ the back of the shirt is protected.
   Ⓒ the fabric doesn't burn.
   Ⓓ the design is easier to pin onto the front of the shirt.

2. Which clue word or words signals the reason that letters should be drawn backward?
   Ⓐ so that
   Ⓑ if
   Ⓒ since
   Ⓓ because

Work with a partner. Talk about your answers to questions 1 and 2. Tell why you chose the answers you did.

Remember: A cause is the reason that something happens. An effect is the result, or what happens because of the cause.

★ To find a cause, look for a reason that something happened. Ask yourself, "*Why* did it happen?"

★ To find an effect, look for a result, or something that happened. Ask yourself, "*What* happened?"

★ Look for clue words that signal cause and effect, such as *so, so that, since, because, if, reason,* and *as a result.*

Read this report that Anya wrote about her mother. As you read, ask yourself, "*What* are some things that happened to Anya's mother? *Why* did these things happen?" Then answer the questions.

Seeing Past Her Blindness

My mother is legally blind. At age three, she developed an infection that caused her to lose her sight. Since then, she has had to learn special ways to overcome her blindness.

Mom can read by using books that have been recorded on tape or printed in braille. Braille is a reading system for the blind, based on touch. In 1824, Louis Braille, then a 15-year-old blind French student, invented the system. In braille, letters, numbers, and punctuation marks are printed as units of small, raised dots. Blind people read braille by running their fingertips over the dots. There is also a special computer for blind people that reads printed material aloud. But Mom doesn't own the machine, because it's too expensive.

If my mom goes walking alone, she uses a special cane. It allows her to feel her way in unfamiliar places. Her friend Janice uses a guide dog. Recently, I read about a pair of glasses with a built-in device that sends out sonar waves. When the waves hit an object in the person's path, they bounce back in the form of sound. These sounds help guide the person wearing the glasses.

Mom doesn't think of herself as a person who cannot see. She says that she "sees" fine, just not with her eyes.

3. Why doesn't Anya's mother own the special computer?
   - Ⓐ The computer is too heavy to carry around.
   - Ⓑ She can read braille more quickly.
   - Ⓒ She prefers to listen to recorded books on tape.
   - Ⓓ The computer is very expensive.

4. What happens when waves from sonar glasses hit an object in a person's path?
   - Ⓐ The waves spread out.
   - Ⓑ The object makes a noise.
   - Ⓒ The waves bounce back in the form of sound.
   - Ⓓ The glasses help the person to partially see.

Look at the answer choices for each question. Read why each answer choice is correct or not correct.

3. Why doesn't Anya's mother own the special computer?

Ⓐ The computer is too heavy to carry around.

This answer is not correct because the report does not state that the computer was heavy to carry. The machine might indeed be heavy, but that cause is not revealed in the selection.

Ⓑ She can read braille more quickly.

This answer is not correct because it is never stated in the report.

Ⓒ She prefers to listen to recorded books on tape.

This answer is not correct because it is not something that is mentioned in the report.

● The computer is very expensive.

This answer is correct because it states the reason that Anya's mother doesn't own the machine. The cause is stated directly in the story, after the effect. The clue word because *signals the cause-and-effect relationship.*

4. What happens when waves from sonar glasses hit an object in a person's path?

Ⓐ The waves spread out.

This answer is not correct because it is not a result that Anya mentions in her report.

Ⓑ The object makes a noise.

This answer is not correct because the object itself never makes a sound. Instead, it is the waves bouncing back after hitting the object that are heard as sounds.

● The waves bounce back in the form of sound.

This answer is correct because it tells the result of sonar waves hitting an object. This effect is stated in the report, after the cause.

Ⓓ The glasses help the person to partially see.

This answer is not correct because the report never states or implies that the glasses help a blind person to partially see. Instead, the glasses help the person to hear sounds that bounce off objects in the person's path.

Sometimes, there are no clue words to signal cause and effect in a reading passage. When there are no clue words, do the following:

★ To find an effect, think about *what* happened.

★ To find a cause, think about *how* or *why* it happened.

★ Think about what you already know about how one thing might cause another thing to happen.

Read this article about why zebras have stripes. Then answer the questions.

In Black and White

Is the zebra a white animal with black stripes? Or is it a black animal with white stripes?

Scientists believe that an early ancestor of the zebra was a dark, horselike animal. This creature had no stripes. Somehow, some of these animals gave birth to babies with light-colored stripes. Because the stripes concealed the young animals' shape, it was harder for enemies to catch these animals. (Solid-colored animals stood out in their surroundings. As a result, they were more likely to be attacked.) Since more of the striped animals survived over many generations, there were more and more striped animals. Eventually, the black-and-white creature known as the zebra was born.

5. Why were the striped animals harder to catch?
   Ⓐ Their stripes concealed their shape.
   Ⓑ Their stripes made them stand out in their surroundings.
   Ⓒ Their stripes blinded their enemies.
   Ⓓ Their stripes were hard to see.

6. Which clue word or words signal the reason that solid-colored animals were more likely to be attacked?
   Ⓐ since
   Ⓑ so
   Ⓒ as a result
   Ⓓ because

7. How did the zebra get its stripes?
   Ⓐ by living a long life
   Ⓑ by hiding in its surroundings
   Ⓒ by finding a way to confuse its enemies
   Ⓓ by gradual change over many generations

8. Because scientists believe that an ancestor was a dark, horselike animal with no stripes, the zebra
   Ⓐ is probably a white animal with black stripes.
   Ⓑ is probably a black animal with white stripes.
   Ⓒ is probably a true horse.
   Ⓓ will probably become all black again over many generations.

Read this Greek myth. Then answer the questions.

Daedalus and Icarus

Daedalus was an inventor who designed a labyrinth for King Minos on the island of Crete. The king had ordered the maze built to hold the Minotaur, a monster who was half man and half bull.

At first, King Minos was pleased with Daedalus. His labyrinth had so many winding paths that the fierce Minotaur could never escape. Later, though, Daedalus offended the king. King Minos got so angry that he imprisoned Daedalus, along with his son, Icarus.

Daedalus immediately set to work on an escape plan. He made two pairs of wings by threading feathers together and fastening them with wax. Then he and his son put on their wings. Just before they flew off, Daedalus warned Icarus not to fly too high or too low. If he flew too low, the sea might wet his wings and make them heavy. If he flew too high, the sun's heat might melt the wax. The best thing, Daedalus told his son, was to follow him closely. Then, flapping their wings up and down, father and son took to the air.

Daedalus flew ahead, but looked back constantly to see how his son was doing. Icarus was so excited to be flying like a bird that he forgot his father's warnings. He climbed higher and higher in the air. At last, he came so near the sun that the wax holding his wings together melted. Icarus plunged into the sea and was drowned. Daedalus recovered his son's body and buried it on a nearby island. That island is now known as Icaria, and the sea into which Icarus fell is called the Icarian Sea.

9. The reason that Daedalus was sent to prison was that
   Ⓐ he insulted the Minotaur.
   Ⓑ he offended King Minos.
   Ⓒ he allowed the Minotaur to escape from the labyrinth.
   Ⓓ he played a foolish trick on King Minos.

10. Why did Icarus climb higher and higher into the air?
   Ⓐ He was ignoring his father's request.
   Ⓑ He did not realize that he was in danger.
   Ⓒ He forgot about his father's warnings.
   Ⓓ He thought that his father was mistaken about the danger.

11. What happened as a result of Icarus's flying too high?
   Ⓐ His wings were burned by the sun's rays.
   Ⓑ His wings became wet and heavy.
   Ⓒ He became tired from the hot sun.
   Ⓓ The sun melted the wax on his wings.

12. The island of Icaria got its name because
   Ⓐ Icarus lived there.
   Ⓑ Icarus fell there.
   Ⓒ Icarus is buried there.
   Ⓓ Icarus flew there.

★ A test question about cause and effect may ask you *what* happened in a reading passage (the effect).

★ A test question about cause and effect may ask *why* something happened (the cause).

★ A test question about cause and effect often contains words such as *because, why, reason, what happened,* or *as a result.*

Here is an article about a famous speech. Read the article. Then do Numbers 13 and 14.

The Gettysburg Address

The Civil War was a war between the Northern states and the Southern states. The people of the North and the South had different views. Mainly, they disagreed about slavery. In 1861, these differences caused the Southern states to break away from the United States. The Northern states didn't want the nation to be divided. So, the "War Between the States" began.

The greatest battle of the war took place in Gettysburg, Pennsylvania, in 1863. The North defeated the South in the Battle of Gettysburg. Both armies, though, suffered many losses. Over 60,000 soldiers died.

President Abraham Lincoln traveled to Gettysburg a few months later. He went there to dedicate part of the battlefield as a cemetery for the dead soldiers. It took Lincoln less than three minutes to give his speech. When he was done, there was hardly any applause. Lincoln thought that his speech had been a failure. He did not realize that most everyone was too deeply moved by his words to clap. Today, many people consider the Gettysburg Address to be the nation's greatest speech.

Recognizing Cause and Effect

13. Why did Lincoln travel to Gettysburg?
     Ⓐ to congratulate the Northern army
     Ⓑ to dedicate part of the battlefield as a cemetery
     Ⓒ to help injured soldiers
     Ⓓ to end the Civil War

Recognizing Cause and Effect

14. Lincoln thought his speech had been a failure because
     Ⓐ few people clapped when he was done.
     Ⓑ it was too short.
     Ⓒ everyone seemed bored.
     Ⓓ the Civil War didn't end.

Here is a story by Rudyard Kipling. Read the story. Then do Numbers 15 and 16.

How the Camel Got His Hump

In the beginning, when the world was so new-and-all, there was a Camel. He lived in the middle of a Howling Desert because he did not want to work. When anybody spoke to him, he said, "Humph!" Just "Humph!" and no more.

Presently, the Horse came to him, with a saddle on his back, and said, "Camel, O Camel, come out and trot like the rest of us."

"Humph!" said the Camel, and the Horse went away and told the Man.

Presently, the Dog came to him, with a stick in his mouth, and said, "Camel, O Camel, come and fetch and carry like the rest of us."

"Humph!" said the Camel, and the Dog went away and told the Man.

Presently, the Ox came to him, with the yoke on his neck, and said, "Camel, O Camel, come and plough like the rest of us."

"Humph!" said the Camel, and the Ox went away and told the Man.

At the end of the day, the Man called the Horse, the Dog, and the Ox together, and said, "I'm very sorry for you but that Humph-thing can't work, or he would have by now. So, you must work double-time to make up for it."

That made the Three very angry. So they held a powwow. Presently, along came the Djinn in charge of All Deserts.

"Djinn of All Deserts," said the Horse, "there's a thing in your Howling Desert with a long neck and legs who won't work. And all he says about it is 'Humph!'"

"Well!" said the Djinn. "I'll humph him if you will kindly wait a minute."

The Djinn found the Camel looking at his reflection in a pool of water.

"My friend," said the Djinn, "what's this I hear of your doing no work?"

"Humph!" said the Camel.

"You've given the Three extra work all on account of your idleness."

"Humph!" said the Camel.

"I shouldn't say that again if I were you," the Djinn warned.

And no sooner had the Camel said "Humph!" again than he saw his back puffing up into a great big humph.

"Do you see that?" said the Djinn. "That's your very own humph that you've brought upon your very own self by not working. You will be able to work now for three days without eating, because you can live on your humph."

And from that day to this, the Camel always wears a hump.

Recognizing Cause and Effect

15. Why did the camel get a hump?
   Ⓐ It was his punishment for doing no work.
   Ⓑ It suddenly appeared when he looked in a pool of water.
   Ⓒ It was a gift from the Djinn.
   Ⓓ It was given to him by the three animals so that he could work longer.

Recognizing Cause and Effect

16. What happened as a result of the Horse's complaining to the Djinn?
   Ⓐ The three animals got more work.
   Ⓑ The Djinn punished the Horse.
   Ⓒ The Djinn went off to scold the Camel.
   Ⓓ The Camel became upset with the Horse.

PART ONE: LEARN ABOUT COMPARING AND CONTRASTING

Read this short history of the buffalo. As you read, think about the ways in which the Plains Indians and the hunters from the East were alike and the ways in which they were different.

At one time, more than 60 million buffalo lived on the Great Plains. For hundreds of years, the Plains Indians hunted the buffalo for food. They killed only the number of buffalo that they needed to survive. They also found ways to use the parts of the buffalo's body that they could not eat. The animal's hide provided clothing and shelter. Its bones and tissues were made into weapons and tools.

In the 1800s, hunters from the East came to the Great Plains. At first, they killed the buffalo mainly for sport. Later, they killed millions of the animals for their hides, which could be turned into leather. The hunters would cut off the valuable hide and then leave the rest of the body to rot. By 1895, fewer than 1,000 buffalo were left.

Ways in which the Plains Indians and the hunters from the East were alike:
They both hunted buffalo on the Great Plains.
They both used the hide of the buffalo they hunted.

Ways in which the Plains Indians and the hunters from the East were different:
The Plains Indians killed only the number of buffalo that they needed to survive, but the hunters killed many buffalo just for sport.
The Plains Indians used the buffalo's entire body for their needs, but the hunters used only the hide.

Finding how two or more things are alike and how they are different is called **comparing and contrasting**. Comparing is finding how people, places, objects, and events are alike. Contrasting is finding how they are different.

★ Clue words that signal how things are alike are *both, same, like, alike,* and *similar.*

★ Clue words that signal how things are different are *but, unlike, different, however,* and *whereas.*

★ If there are no clue words in a reading passage to signal a comparison or a contrast, think about the people, places, objects, or events you read about. Ask yourself, "How are they alike? How are they different?"

Read this speech written by Ryan about his favorite sport, lacrosse. As you read, look for clue words that tell how lacrosse and baggataway are alike and how they are different. Then answer the questions.

My Favorite Sport

My favorite sport is lacrosse. I've been playing this sport as long as I can remember. Lacrosse is one of the oldest and fastest sports in North America. In Canada, it is the national sport.

Lacrosse is played by two teams on a large field. The object of the game is to throw a rubber ball into the opposing team's goal. Players use a long stick with a basket, or pocket, on the end to pass the ball among teammates and move it down the field.

Lacrosse comes from a rugged game that was played in Canada hundreds of years ago. The Algonquin, Huron, and Iroquois nations called the game "baggataway." The Native Americans used a playing stick similar to today's lacrosse stick. But instead of a rubber ball, they used a ball made of hair covered with deerskin.

Unlike lacrosse, baggataway was partly a religious ceremony. It was also an excellent way to get warriors into top physical condition. Baggataway teams were much larger than modern lacrosse teams. They sometimes had up to a thousand players! Several miles often separated the goals. Games could last for two or three days.

Some of the first French settlers in Canada played baggataway with the Native Americans. The French gave the sport its present name. They thought that the playing stick looked like a staff carried by French bishops. As a result, the stick came to be called *la crosse*.

1. How are lacrosse and baggataway alike?
   Ⓐ Both games last several days.
   Ⓑ Both games are played by using long sticks and a ball.
   Ⓒ Both games are played only in Canada.
   Ⓓ Both games are played on the same size playing field.

2. Which clue word or words signal that lacrosse and baggataway are different?
   Ⓐ but
   Ⓑ similar
   Ⓒ unlike
   Ⓓ as a result

Work with a partner. Talk about your answers to questions 1 and 2. Tell why you chose the answers you did.

Remember: Comparing is finding ways in which things are alike.
Contrasting is finding ways in which things are different.

★ Look for clue words that signal a likeness, or comparison, such as *both*, *same*, *like*, *alike*, and *similar*.

★ Look for clue words that signal a difference, or contrast, such as *but*, *unlike*, *different*, *however*, and *whereas*.

★ If there are no clue words, think about the ways in which the people, places, objects, and events in the reading passage are being compared and contrasted.

Read this poem about the ways in which an adult and a child question the world. In the poem, the questions are referred to as serving-men. As you read, ask yourself, "How are the views of the adult and the child alike? How are their views different?" Then answer the questions.

I keep six honest serving-men
(They taught me all I knew);
Their names are What and Why and When
And How and Where and Who.
I send them over land and sea,
I send them east and west;
But after they have worked for me,
I give them all a rest.

I let them rest from nine till five,
For I am busy then,
As well as breakfast, lunch, and tea,
For they are hungry men.

But different folk have different views;
I know a person small—
She keeps ten million serving-men,
Who get no rest at all!
She sends 'em abroad on her own affairs,
From the second she opens her eyes—
One million Hows, two million Wheres,
And seven million Whys!

by Rudyard Kipling

3. In what way are the views of the adult and the child alike?
   Ⓐ Both ask the same number of questions.
   Ⓑ Both ask questions the entire day.
   Ⓒ Both take a break from asking questions during the day.
   Ⓓ Both ask questions, such as How, Where, and Why.

4. Which clue word signals that there is a difference between the views of the adult and the child?
   Ⓐ similar
   Ⓑ but
   Ⓒ unlike
   Ⓓ whereas

Look at the answer choices for each question. Read why each answer choice is correct or not correct.

3. In what way are the views of the adult and the child alike?

(A) Both ask the same number of questions.

This answer is not correct because the poem suggests that the adult asks a few questions during the day, but the child asks millions of questions.

(B) Both ask questions the entire day.

This answer is not correct because the poem states that the adult lets his serving-men rest from nine till five, for he is busy then.

(C) Both take a break from asking questions during the day.

This answer is not correct because the poem states that the adult gives his serving-men a rest after they have worked for him. The child, though, keeps her serving-men busy all day, "from the second she opens her eyes."

● Both ask questions, such as How, Where, and Why.

This answer is correct because the poem is about an adult and a child asking questions. The difference between them is the number of questions they ask.

4. Which clue word signals that there is a difference between the views of the adult and the child?

(A) similar

This answer is not correct because the word similar *is usually used to compare things, not contrast them. Also, the word* similar *is not used in the poem.*

● but

This answer is correct because the word but *introduces the line that signals a difference: "But different folk have different views." Note that the word* different *is also used to signal a contrast.*

(C) unlike

This answer is not correct because the word unlike *is not used in the poem.*

(D) whereas

This answer is not correct because the word whereas *is not used in the poem.*

Sometimes, there are no clue words in a reading passage to signal that things are being compared or contrasted. When there are no clue words,

★ think about the people, places, objects, or events that you read about. Ask yourself, "How are they alike? How are they different?"

★ think about what is being compared or contrasted. Ask yourself, "In what ways are they compared? In what ways are they contrasted?"

Read this story about a contest winner. Then answer the questions.

Names Can Be Misleading

Simon won a trip to an island in the North Atlantic Ocean. His choices were Greenland or Iceland. Simon didn't want to visit Iceland. Its name made him cold. Greenland sounded like a much better place. Simon didn't know that Greenland isn't really green. In fact, it's probably one of the least green places on earth. Most of Greenland lies above the Arctic Circle and is covered with thick ice. In 982 A.D., the Viking leader Eric the Red established a colony there. He hoped to attract more settlers to the frozen island, so he called it "Greenland." The island population, however, stayed small. Today, most Greenlanders live near the southwest coast. It is the warmest part of the island. It is also the only area where grass and trees grow.

Simon should have studied his geography better. He would have known that Iceland is south of Greenland. Only the northern tip of Iceland touches the Arctic Circle. Iceland has far more green land than its neighbor. Part of Iceland is covered by ice, but the island also has hundreds of natural hot springs and volcanoes. Greenland is 840,000 square miles in area and has about 60,000 people, whereas Iceland is 20 times smaller in area and has at least four times as many people. Most Icelanders also live on the milder, southwest coast.

5. How are Greenland and Iceland alike?
   Ⓐ Both lie mostly above the Arctic Circle.
   Ⓑ Both are in the North Atlantic Ocean.
   Ⓒ Both are the same size.
   Ⓓ Both are mostly covered with ice.

6. In what way are the islands different?
   Ⓐ Greenland is smaller.
   Ⓑ Greenland has more people.
   Ⓒ Most people in Iceland live in the middle of the country.
   Ⓓ Only Iceland has hot springs and volcanoes.

7. Which of these tells one thing that the islands have in common?
   Ⓐ The southwest coast is the warmest part of each island.
   Ⓑ Eric the Red discovered each island.
   Ⓒ Neither island has any green land.
   Ⓓ Both islands have a large population.

8. The clue word *whereas* is used to contrast the islands'
   Ⓐ size and population.
   Ⓑ size and location.
   Ⓒ population and climate.
   Ⓓ appearance and location.

Read this chart, which describes some ways dolphins and porpoises are alike and different. Then answer the questions.

Quality	Dolphins	Porpoises
Must surface to breath	√	√
Have blowhole on top of head	√	√
Live in deep waters and near coast	√	
Live mostly in coastal waters		√
Swim at speeds of 20 to 25 mph	√	√
Feed mostly on fish	√	√
Have a long, pointed snout	√	
Have a short, rounded snout		√
Have cone-shaped teeth	√	
Have flat, spade-shaped teeth		√
Have a long, thin body	√	
Have a steeply sloping forehead	√	
Have a gently sloping forehead		√
Known for their intelligence	√	√
Can be trained to perform tricks	√	√
Produce sounds underwater and listen to the echoes to find food	√	√

dolphin

porpoise

9. Which of these tells one way dolphins and porpoises are alike?
   Ⓐ Both have cone-shaped teeth.
   Ⓑ Both live mostly in deep waters.
   Ⓒ Both can perform tricks.
   Ⓓ Both are the same size.

10. One way that dolphins and porpoises are different is that
   Ⓐ only dolphins can produce sounds underwater.
   Ⓑ porpoises have a more steeply sloping forehead.
   Ⓒ porpoises swim faster than dolphins.
   Ⓓ dolphins have a longer snout.

11. What three qualities do dolphins have in common with porpoises?
   Ⓐ have blowhole, are intelligent, produce sounds underwater
   Ⓑ must surface to breathe, swim at fast speeds, live in deep waters
   Ⓒ have a rounded snout, feed mostly on fish, are intelligent
   Ⓓ have flat teeth, have a pointed snout, live in coastal waters

12. Which of these is true?
   Ⓐ Porpoises are different from dolphins in every way.
   Ⓑ Porpoises do mostly the same things that dolphins do.
   Ⓒ Dolphins look like porpoises.
   Ⓓ Dolphins are just like porpoises, except that they are smarter.

★ A test question about comparing and contrasting may ask you how things are alike or how they are different.

★ A test question about comparing and contrasting usually contains a clue word. Words such as *same*, *like*, *alike*, and *similar* signal that you are to compare things. Words such as *different*, *unlike*, or *not like* signal that you are to contrast things.

Here is a story about a speed skater. Read the story. Then do Numbers 13 and 14.

On the Cutting Edge

Tory is a speed skater. Her idol is Bonnie Blair, the Olympic gold-medal winner. When Tory started speed skating, she read a lot about the sport. She was surprised to learn how much it has changed recently.

Until 1997, speed skaters wore skates in which the entire boot was firmly attached to the blade. Today, most speed skaters wear clap skates. The heel of a clap skate is not attached to the blade. A hinge with a spring holds the toe of the boot to the blade. When a skater pushes off, the heel lifts up, leaving the entire blade on the ice longer. When the skater's entire foot lifts off the ice, the blade snaps back to the heel, making a clapping sound.

On traditional speed skates, athletes push off from the back of the skate. They rely on their thigh muscles for power. On clap skates, athletes push from the front of the skate and use both their calf muscles and thigh muscles. The extra muscle power enables the skaters to extend their legs out farther. The more the leg extends, the longer the stride. The longer the stride is, the faster the speed.

Speed skaters who had trained on traditional skates for years had to learn new techniques to use clap skates. Some athletes had a hard time adjusting to the new skates. Unknown athletes who had figured out how to use clap skates began breaking world records.

Tory is on the cutting edge in her sport. She has never skated on anything but clap skates. But if she ever becomes the next Bonnie Blair, who knows what she'll be wearing on her feet!

Comparing and Contrasting

13. In what way is a traditional speed skate different from a clap skate?
    - Ⓐ A traditional skate is attached at the toe, but a clap skate is not.
    - Ⓑ A clap skate is attached only at the toe.
    - Ⓒ The boot of a clap skate is firmly fixed to the blade.
    - Ⓓ Only the traditional skate requires athletes to use their thigh muscles.

Comparing and Contrasting

14. How are traditional skates and clap skates alike?
    - Ⓐ Both have a blade that remains on the ice the same amount of time.
    - Ⓑ Both require the skater to push from the back of the skate.
    - Ⓒ Both pack the same amount of power and speed.
    - Ⓓ Both have boots and blades.

Here are a fable from Aesop and a Native American folktale. Read the stories.
Then do Numbers 15 and 16.

One day, Hare made fun of Tortoise for being so slow on his feet. Much to Hare's surprise, Tortoise challenged him to a race. The Hare was amused at the idea. "Very well," he replied. "Let's try and see."

When the race began, Hare dashed off, leaving Tortoise behind. Soon Hare was so far ahead that he decided to take a nap. Meanwhile, Tortoise plodded on and on. When Hare awoke at last, he was surprised that Tortoise was nowhere in sight. Hare raced his fastest to the finish line, only to find that Tortoise had already won.

Heron and Hummingbird lived together on the shores of the Atlantic Ocean. One day Hummingbird challenged Heron to a race.

"I can't race you," Heron said. "I almost never fly, and you seem never to sit. You are so swift and agile, and I am so slow and clumsy."

But Hummingbird kept after Heron to race, until one day Heron agreed.

They decided to race from the Atlantic Ocean in the East to the Pacific Ocean in the West.

They drew a line at the water's edge and began their race.

Heron had barely lifted his wings and tucked up his feet, when Hummingbird was out of sight. But Heron kept flapping and flying, and it wasn't long before he began to glide along with a slow and steady motion.

At nightfall, Hummingbird flew to a tree and stopped for the night, while Heron continued his flight. But it wasn't until daybreak that he reached the tree where Hummingbird was sleeping.

The sun had not even reached mid-sky before Hummingbird had already passed Heron on the following day.

That night Hummingbird rested again, but this time she was passed by Heron, before midnight.

The next day Hummingbird didn't pass Heron until noon.

On the third night Heron caught up with Hummingbird well before midnight, and Hummingbird did not pass Heron on the following day until late afternoon.

Once more Hummingbird rested at nightfall, and again she was passed by Heron, who still hadn't slept but had flown with a slow but steady rhythm toward his destination. The next morning Heron arrived at the Pacific Ocean far ahead of Hummingbird, who was surprised to learn, when she finally arrived at the ocean's edge, that she had lost the race.

Comparing and Contrasting

15. What is similar about the two stories?
    (A) In both stories, a quicker animal challenged a slower animal to a race.
    (B) In both stories, a quicker animal made fun of a slower animal.
    (C) In both stories, Hare and Hummingbird rested each night.
    (D) In both stories, the slower animal won the race.

Comparing and Contrasting

16. The stories are different because
    (A) the birds' race lasted longer.
    (B) Hare wanted to race, but Hummingbird did not.
    (C) Tortoise was slow but Heron was not.
    (D) Hummingbird was less certain than Hare about winning the race.

STRATEGY 6

PART ONE: LEARN ABOUT MAKING PREDICTIONS

Read this fable from Aesop. As you read, think about what might happen next in the fable.

Once upon a time, a group of mice got together. They met to discuss the best way to protect themselves against their common enemy, the cat. After several suggestions were made, a young mouse stood up and said, "I think I have an idea that will guarantee our safety. We should attach a small bell around the cat's neck. Its tinkling will warn us of her approach."

The other mice warmly applauded this proposal. They were about to approve it when a wise old mouse got upon his feet.

Think about what you read and what you already know about cats and mice. Make a good guess about what might happen next. Then continue reading to see how close your guess is to what actually happens.

"I agree with everyone that the plan before us is very clever," said the wise old mouse. "May I ask, however, who is going to put the bell on the cat?"

What happened next in the story was **the wise old mouse told the other mice that someone was going to have to put the bell around the cat's neck.**

When you think about what might happen next in a reading passage, you are **making a prediction**. Making a prediction is a way of using clues from a reading passage, as well as things you already know, to make a good guess about what might happen next.

★ Clues are often in the title of a reading passage. Read the title, and then make a prediction about what you will be reading.

★ Clues are often in the facts and details in a reading passage. Details about the things characters do and say often help you make a prediction about what they might do or say later in the story.

★ Clues are often in any pictures included with a story. Pictures often show something that is happening or will happen soon.

Read this news article. As you read, ask yourself, "What does the headline tell me about what I will be reading? Which facts and details will help me predict what will happen next?" Then answer the questions.

The Shipping News

January 31, 1999

No More Dots and Dashes

At midnight tonight, Morse code ends as the official language of the sea. For more than a century, ships in trouble have used Morse code to signal other ships or rescue stations on shore. Now a new high-tech system will be replacing the famous code.

Morse code is named for its inventor, Samuel F. Morse. Morse developed the code in 1832 to send messages. Dots and dashes represent numbers and letters of the alphabet. The dots are short electric signals, and the dashes are long signals. With help from others, Morse later invented a telegraph on which to send his code. Morse code was not useful at sea, however, until the wireless telegraph was invented, in the late 1890s. The most popular Morse code message at sea is SOS, or dot-dot-dot dash-dash-dash dot-dot-dot.

As of tomorrow, international law requires all freighters and passenger ships to have the new high-tech system. It automatically signals to rescue stations ashore when a ship is in danger. The signals give the ship's name and its exact location. With this new system, no ship should ever vanish without a trace. More lives will be saved.

The new system, though, still presents risks. Some poorer countries may not be able to afford the safer equipment. They may ignore the law. Crews and passengers could be in greater danger for a while.

1. What do you think will most likely happen in the future?
   Ⓐ Sailors will have a lot of problems getting used to the new system.
   Ⓑ Morse code will be replaced on all ships.
   Ⓒ Ships will go back to using Morse code because it's less risky.
   Ⓓ No ship will ever sink again.

2. Where did you find clues to help you make your prediction?
   Ⓐ in the title of the news article
   Ⓑ in the picture that was included with the news article
   Ⓒ in the details about the high-tech signaling system
   Ⓓ in the details about what Samuel Morse did

 Work with a partner. Talk about your answers to questions 1 and 2. Tell why you chose the answers you did.

Remember: Making a prediction is a way of using clues from a reading passage, as well as things you already know, to make a good guess about what might happen next.

★ Look for clues in a reading passage to help you predict what might happen next. Clues are often in the title, in the facts and details, and in any pictures.

★ Ask yourself, "What do I already know about the things I am reading about?"

Read this poem about a knight's search for a land of riches. As you read, look for clues that will help you predict what happened to the knight. Then answer the questions.

Eldorado
by Edgar Allan Poe

Gaily bedight,
A gallant knight,
   In sunshine and in shadow,
Had journeyed long,
Singing a song,
   In search of Eldorado.

But he grew old—
This knight so bold—
   And o'er his heart a shadow
Fell as he found
No spot of ground
   That looked like Eldorado.

And, as his strength
Failed him at length,
   He met a pilgrim shadow—
"Shadow," said he,
"Where can it be—
   This land of Eldorado?"

"Over the mountains
Of the moon,
   Down the Valley of the Shadow,
Ride, boldly ride,"
The shadow replied,—
   "If you seek for Eldorado!"

3. What probably happened to the knight?
   - Ⓐ He found Eldorado by going over the mountains and through the valley.
   - Ⓑ He realized that he had been dreaming.
   - Ⓒ He died a rich and happy man.
   - Ⓓ He died, having never found Eldorado.

4. How might things have been different if the knight had found Eldorado?
   - Ⓐ He might have never grown old.
   - Ⓑ He might have become very greedy.
   - Ⓒ He might have still been happy and bold.
   - Ⓓ He might have never needed advice from a stranger.

Look at the answer choices for each question. Read why each answer choice is correct or not correct.

3. What probably happened to the knight?

Ⓐ He found Eldorado by going over the mountains and through the valley.

This answer is not correct because the mountains mentioned in the poem were on the moon.

Ⓑ He realized that he had been dreaming.

This answer is not correct because there are no clues in the poem to suggest that the knight had been sleeping or dreaming.

Ⓒ He died a rich and happy man.

This answer is not correct because nothing in the poem suggests that the knight would find Eldorado. The shadow he met essentially told him to end his search for Eldorado, for no such place existed.

● He died, having never found Eldorado.

This answer is correct because details in the poem state that the knight had grown old and weak during his search. Also, the shadow tells the knight to ride "Over the mountains/Of the moon,/Down the Valley of the Shadow." These words suggest that Eldorado is not a real place.

4. How might things have been different if the knight had found Eldorado?

Ⓐ He might have never grown old.

This answer is not correct because no clues in the poem suggest that people stay young in Eldorado. Even if the knight had found Eldorado when he was still young, he would have still grown old.

Ⓑ He might have become very greedy.

This answer is not correct because no clues suggest that the knight was a greedy person or would become greedy once he found Eldorado.

● He might have still been happy and bold.

This answer is correct because details in the poem state that the knight was happy and bold when he began his search for Eldorado. After he grew old and had still not found the land of riches, he became heavy hearted. If the knight had found Eldorado, he would have had no reason to become less spirited.

Ⓓ He might have never needed advice from a stranger.

This answer is not correct because there is no way to tell whether this prediction was likely. If the knight had found Eldorado, he would not have sought help from the shadow. However, he might have still needed advice from other people at certain times in his life.

★ Look for clues in the reading passage that tell what the characters are like.
Think about how the characters behave, how they are feeling, and the things
they say and do.

★ Link the clues with what you know from your own experiences. Ask yourself,
"What have people like this character done in a similar situation?"

Read this narrative about a true event. Then answer the questions.

The Mutiny on the *Bounty*

The year was 1789. The British ship the *Bounty* sailed in the South Pacific Ocean.
Its mission was to bring breadfruit trees all the way from Tahiti to British settlements
in the Caribbean Sea. The captain of the *Bounty* was William Bligh. Captain Bligh was
an excellent sailor, but he was a cruel commander. He controlled his crew with harsh
treatment. Many of the men hated him.

One of the crew was Fletcher Christian. The other sailors respected Christian,
and when he spoke that forbidden word—*mutiny*—the men listened. Mutiny meant
disobeying the captain and taking over the ship. Mutiny was forbidden by law.
But the crew had reached their breaking point. Mutiny it would be! If British sailors
who mutinied were ever caught, they would be hanged! And a captain who
could not prevent a mutiny did not escape without punishment either.

The crew seized control of the *Bounty*. They put Captain Bligh into a small boat.
Eighteen sailors refused to go along with the mutiny. They were put in the boat
with Bligh. The boat was set adrift in the vast ocean.

The mutineers had to hide in a place where no British sailing vessel would ever
find them. Eventually, they sailed the *Bounty* toward a tiny mountainous island
more than one thousand miles southeast of Tahiti. No people lived there. So it was
that Fletcher Christian and eight other mutineers, along with six men and
twelve women of Polynesia, came to live on Pitcairn Island.

Meanwhile, Captain Bligh and the others sailed their small vessel 3,500 miles
to safety. Eventually, they returned to England.

5. What probably happened to the *Bounty?*
   Ⓐ The mutineers sailed it to England.
   Ⓑ The mutineers destroyed it.
   Ⓒ The British navy found it.
   Ⓓ The mutineers lived in it.

6. Which clue hinted that Captain Bligh would
   be able to sail his small boat to safety?
   Ⓐ He had eighteen sailors with him.
   Ⓑ He was in a boat that was small.
   Ⓒ He controlled his crew with
     harsh treatment.
   Ⓓ He was an excellent sailor.

7. What most likely happened after
   Captain Bligh returned to England?
   Ⓐ He was blamed for losing his ship.
   Ⓑ He never sailed again.
   Ⓒ He was given a new ship.
   Ⓓ He was punished for being cruel
     to his men.

8. If the British navy found the mutineers,
   the mutineers would probably have
   Ⓐ surrendered without a fight.
   Ⓑ apologized for what they had done.
   Ⓒ seized control of the British ship.
   Ⓓ been hanged for their crime.

Read this Greek myth about King Midas. Then answer the questions.

The Golden Touch

There once was a Greek king named Midas, who was famous for his beautiful rose garden. One day, the god Dionysus was traveling through the king's lands. His old teacher, Silenus, traveled with him. Silenus was a satyr, a creature that is half human and half goat. Like all satyrs, Silenus was often careless. In due time, he got lost and fell asleep in King Midas's rose garden. Some peasants found the satyr and took him to the king. King Midas recognized Silenus and treated him kindly for the next ten days. During this time, Silenus entertained the king with many wondrous tales. On the eleventh day, the king brought Silenus to Dionysus. Dionysus was grateful to King Midas for taking care of his teacher. So, he offered to grant the king any wish. King Midas wished that everything he touched should be turned to gold.

Dionysus thought the wish was unwise, but he granted it anyway. Midas was so excited about his new power that he began testing it out at once. Everything he touched—the earth, his roses, the pillars of his palace—instantly turned to gold.

For a brief while, King Midas was happy. But then he began to regret his greedy wish. Whenever he tried to put any food or drink in his mouth, it also turned to gold. Despite all of his wealth, the king was hungry and thirsty. Then, one day, he truly realized how great a mistake he had made. He accidentally killed his daughter by turning her to gold when he touched her.

The heartbroken king pleaded with Dionysus to undo the wish. Dionysus took pity on King Midas and told him to bathe in the river Pactolus.

9. What mostly likely happened after King Midas stepped into the river?
   Ⓐ He drowned.
   Ⓑ His golden touch washed away.
   Ⓒ His greed disappeared.
   Ⓓ His daughter came back to life.

10. Which clue first hints that the king's wish would be a mistake?
   Ⓐ Dionysus thought the wish was unwise.
   Ⓑ King Midas began to regret his wish.
   Ⓒ The king accidentally killed his daughter.
   Ⓓ The king was hungry and thirsty.

11. If King Midas were ever granted a wish again, he would probably
   Ⓐ refuse to make the wish.
   Ⓑ make another greedy wish.
   Ⓒ make a wiser choice.
   Ⓓ wish that he had Dionysus's power.

12. If his daughter had not died, the king would have probably
   Ⓐ never asked Dionysus to undo the wish.
   Ⓑ still asked Dionysus to undo the wish.
   Ⓒ remained happy with his wealth.
   Ⓓ shared his wealth with others.

★ A test question about making a prediction may ask you to make a good guess about what will happen next in a reading passage, or what might happen in the future.

★ A test question about making a prediction usually contains the words *predict*, *probably*, or *most likely*.

Here is a report about a famous woman in history. Read the report. Then do Numbers 13 and 14.

Reporting on a Remarkable Reporter

The woman whom I most admire was a reporter. She called herself Nellie Bly. I chose Bly for my report because I'd like to be a reporter too.

Nellie Bly was born in Pennsylvania in 1867. Her real name was Elizabeth Cochran. When Elizabeth was eighteen, she read a troubling newspaper essay. It stated that respectable women should not work outside the home. Elizabeth wrote back to the newspaper. In her letter, she stated her own views about women's independence.

The newspaper editor liked Elizabeth's writing so much that he hired her. He convinced her to take a pen name. She chose the name of a character from a popular song. "Nellie Bly" soon became known for writing about life in slums and factories.

As a reporter, Bly sometimes went undercover. In 1887, she pretended to be ill so as to gain entry to a hospital for people with mental illness. Bly spent ten days as a patient there. Her articles about the experience led to many improvements at the hospital.

In 1888, Bly decided that she would circle the globe. She had recently read Jules Verne's adventure novel *Around the World in Eighty Days*. Bly hoped to beat the record set by Verne's imaginary character, Phileas Fogg.

Bly began her journey on November 14, 1889. During the 24,899-mile trip, she traveled by boat, train, and even mule cart. On January 26, 1890, she returned home, setting a record of 72 days, 6 hours, and 11 minutes.

Making Predictions

13. Predict what Bly probably did next.
    - Ⓐ She decided never to leave home again.
    - Ⓑ She called Jules Verne to boast about her victory.
    - Ⓒ She left her job as a reporter.
    - Ⓓ She wrote news stories about her experiences.

Making Predictions

14. Predict how people reacted to Bly's achievement.
    - Ⓐ They were angry that a woman had broken a man's record.
    - Ⓑ They were excited that a person had traveled that fast.
    - Ⓒ They were convinced that she had cheated.
    - Ⓓ They were upset that Bly did not realize that her place was at home.

Here is a legend about a Swiss hero. Read the legend. Then do Numbers 15 and 16.

The Legend of Wilhelm Tell

Long ago, in the heart of the Alps, there were three little countries called Schwytz, Ur, and Unterwalken. The people of these countries lived happily until Austria, their large, powerful neighbor, took control of their land. The Austrian governors ruled harshly. They forced their subjects to pay heavy taxes and obey unfair laws.

The most hated of the governors was a cruel man named Gessler. One day, Gessler stuck his hat on a pole in the marketplace. He told his soldiers to make everyone who passed by bow down before the hat.

One morning, a brave hunter from the mountains went to the marketplace with his son. The hunter's name was Wilhelm Tell, and he was famous for his skill with a bow. When Tell and his son passed the hat on the pole, they did not bow, for they did not know about Gessler's order. The guards stopped them and ordered them to bow to the hat, but Tell refused. So, the soldiers arrested him and summoned Gessler. The governor knew of Tell's talent as an archer. He told Tell that he would set him free if he could shoot an apple off his son's head. If he missed, Tell would die.

While his son stood straight and still, Tell took aim. He pierced the apple right through the center. Gessler could not accept his defeat. He spotted a second arrow hidden inside Tell's shirt and demanded to know why it was there. Tell boldly replied that if he had killed his son, the other arrow would have been used against Gessler.

Gessler ordered his soldiers to arrest this villain. They bound Tell in ropes and put him aboard a small boat. As the boat was crossing the lake toward Gessler's castle on the other side, a violent storm arose. The soldiers could not handle the boat, and they begged Gessler to let them untie Tell. Tell rowed hard and strong until he was close to shore. Then he dropped the oars, jumped onto the bank, and fled.

Making Predictions

15. What do you think Gessler did next?
    - Ⓐ He made his soldiers go after Tell.
    - Ⓑ He told his men to leave Tell alone.
    - Ⓒ He fell overboard and drowned.
    - Ⓓ He used a bow and arrow to shoot at Tell.

Making Predictions

16. If Tell was found, he would probably
    - Ⓐ surrender quietly.
    - Ⓑ beg for his life to be spared.
    - Ⓒ defend himself.
    - Ⓓ admit he was wrong.

REVIEW STRATEGIES 4–6

PART ONE: READ A FOLKTALE

Here is a folktale from India. Read the folktale. Then do Numbers 1 through 6.

The Tiger, the Brahman, and the Jackal

Once upon a time, there was a caged tiger. He struggled to escape through the cage's narrow bars, and sobbed with rage when he failed.

By chance, a poor Brahman came by.

"Let me out of this cage," cried the tiger.

"No, my friend," replied the Brahman, "you would probably eat me if I did."

"On the contrary," swore the tiger. "I would be forever grateful and would be your servant for the rest of your days!"

The Brahman still wouldn't let the tiger out. But as the tiger continued his wailing and sobbing, the Brahman's heart softened. At last, he consented to open the cage door.

The tiger sprang out of the cage and seized the Brahman. "What a fool you are!" cried the tiger. "Now there's nothing to stop me from eating you."

The Brahman pleaded for his life. At last, he convinced the tiger to let him question the first animal he saw. That animal would decide the fairness of the tiger's actions. The Brahman promised to accept the animal's decision, no matter what.

Just then, a jackal came walking by. The Brahman told the jackal his story. "How very confusing!" the jackal replied. "Would you mind telling me over again?"

The Brahman repeated his story, but the jackal still could not understand.

"Everything just seems to go in one ear and out the other," the jackal said. "Perhaps if I go to the place where it all happened, I shall be able to give you my opinion."

So they returned to the cage, where the hungry tiger was waiting. As the Brahman began to explain the entire matter again, the jackal exclaimed, "Oh, dear! Oh, dear! Where are my wits? Let me see—you were in the cage, and the tiger came walking by—"

"No, you fool!" interrupted the tiger. "I was in the cage."

"Of course!" cried the jackal, pretending to tremble with fright. "I was in the cage. No, that's not right. Let me see—the tiger was in the Brahman, and the cage came walking by. No, that's not it, either. Oh my! I shall never understand."

"Look here," the tiger shouted angrily. "I am the tiger. And that is the Brahman. And that is the cage. And I was in the cage. Do you understand?"

"Well, no," the jackal replied. "Please tell me, how did you get in?"

The tiger finally lost his patience. He jumped into the cage and cried, "This way! Now do you understand what happened?"

"Perfectly!" the jackal declared, as he shut the cage door. Then he turned to the Brahman with a smile and said, "Now let us leave matters as they were!"

Recognizing Cause and Effect

1. The Brahman opened the cage door at last because
   - Ⓐ he wasn't very afraid of tigers.
   - Ⓑ he knew tigers didn't like to eat Brahmans.
   - Ⓒ he felt sorry for the weeping tiger.
   - Ⓓ he thought the tiger would make a good servant.

Comparing and Contrasting

4. How were the Brahman and the jackal different?
   - Ⓐ The jackal was more afraid of the tiger.
   - Ⓑ Only the Brahman didn't trust the tiger.
   - Ⓒ Only the Brahman was tricked.
   - Ⓓ The tiger thought that only the jackal was a fool.

Recognizing Cause and Effect

2. What happened when the Brahman told the jackal his story?
   - Ⓐ The jackal appeared to be quite confused.
   - Ⓑ The jackal pretended to be afraid.
   - Ⓒ The jackal asked the tiger if the story was true.
   - Ⓓ The jackal told the Brahman that the tiger had been unfair.

Making Predictions

5. Predict what the tiger will most likely do next.
   - Ⓐ He will sob with rage.
   - Ⓑ He will trick the Brahman again.
   - Ⓒ He will escape by bending the bars of the cage.
   - Ⓓ He will apologize for losing his patience.

Comparing and Contrasting

3. How were the tiger and the jackal alike?
   - Ⓐ Both lost their patience easily.
   - Ⓑ Both were sly creatures.
   - Ⓒ Both wanted to eat the Brahman.
   - Ⓓ Both became easily confused.

Making Predictions

6. If the Brahman came across a caged tiger again, he would probably
   - Ⓐ free the animal.
   - Ⓑ ignore the animal.
   - Ⓒ seek the jackal's advice.
   - Ⓓ ask the tiger if it is hungry.

Here is an article about the life of two scientists. Read the article.
Then do Numbers 7 through 12.

Women in the Field

Scientists Jane Goodall and Dian Fossey were both known for their work with apes. Goodall observed chimpanzees. Fossey studied mountain gorillas.

Jane Goodall was born in Great Britain in 1934. As a young girl, she dreamed of going to Africa to study animals. In her twenties, Goodall's dream came true. She took a trip to Kenya. While visiting the country, she worked for Louis and Mary Leakey. The famous couple was digging for human fossils. Louis Leakey encouraged Goodall to study chimpanzees in the wild. He got funds for her fieldwork, which began in 1960, in Tanzania.

It took Goodall more than a year to win the trust of the chimpanzees she was studying. Finally, they allowed her to get close enough to observe them. Goodall made two surprising discoveries. She learned that chimpanzees eat other animals. Most scientists at that time thought that chimpanzees only ate fruits and vegetables. She also discovered that chimpanzees make and use tools. Goodall spent the next 25 years in the jungle, observing chimp behavior. Today, she spends her time writing books and speaking about the need to protect these wild animals.

Dian Fossey was born in San Francisco in 1932. As a young woman, Fossey read a book about mountain gorillas that captured her interest. In 1963, she traveled to Africa to see the animals. She also visited Louis Leakey. In 1966, Leakey arranged for Fossey to study mountain gorillas in their natural habit.

Fossey set up camp on a hillside in Rwanda. There, she quickly gained the trust of the gorillas by imitating them. Fossey was able to observe the animals at close range. Through her observations, she discovered that gorillas are not as fierce as they look. They are generally peaceful animals. After poachers illegally hunted and killed several gorillas, Fossey worked hard to protect them. She described her work in the 1983 book *Gorillas in the Mist*. In 1985, Fossey was murdered. Many people suspect that the poachers killed her too.

Jane Goodall

Dian Fossey

Recognizing Cause and Effect

7. Goodall went to Tanzania because
   (A) she had always wanted to go to Africa.
   (B) she wanted to work for the Leakeys.
   (C) Louis Leakey had gotten funds for her to do fieldwork with chimps.
   (D) it was the only place where she could observe chimps in the wild.

Recognizing Cause and Effect

8. How did Fossey gain the gorillas' trust?
   (A) by patiently waiting a year for them to accept her
   (B) by imitating them
   (C) by working hard to protect them
   (D) by observing them at close range

Comparing and Contrasting

9. How were Jane Goodall and Dian Fossey alike?
   (A) Both worked in Tanzania.
   (B) Both were British scientists.
   (C) Both went to Africa in 1963.
   (D) Both had Louis Leakey's support.

Comparing and Contrasting

10. What is one way that Goodall and Fossey were different?
    (A) Only Fossey wrote a book.
    (B) It took Goodall more time to win the trust of her apes.
    (C) Only Fossey observed animals in their own environment.
    (D) Only Goodall made interesting discoveries.

Making Predictions

11. Predict how Fossey felt when the gorillas were killed.
    (A) She was deeply saddened.
    (B) She was not at all concerned.
    (C) She was slightly annoyed.
    (D) She was greatly insulted.

Making Predictions

12. Predict which of these most likely happened after Fossey's book was published.
    (A) The poachers stopped killing the gorillas.
    (B) People became more aware of her work and the need to protect the gorillas.
    (C) People refused to believe that gorillas are peaceful animals.
    (D) More scientists went to Tanzania to study gorillas.

PART ONE: LEARN ABOUT FINDING WORD MEANING IN CONTEXT

Read this paragraph about Amelia Bloomer. As you read, think about the meaning of the word *advocate* in the first sentence.

Amelia Jenks Bloomer was a famous advocate of women's rights. She supported the idea that women should have the same rights as men. She even argued in favor of women's wearing of pants. Whenever she appeared in public, Bloomer wore loose pants under a short skirt. Eventually, these pants were called *bloomers*.

You can figure out the meaning of the word *advocate* by looking at the words and phrases around it. The phrases *supported the idea* and *argued in favor of* are clues to the meaning of the word *advocate*.

The meaning of the word *advocate* is "a person who supports an idea or argues in favor of something."

When you use clues in a reading passage to figure out the meaning of an unknown word, you are **finding word meaning in context**. The words and phrases around an unknown word often provide clues to the word's meaning. These clues are called **context clues**.

★ Context clues are often in the sentence where the unknown word appears. They can also be in the sentences before and after the word.

★ Clues about the meaning of an unknown word are often found by thinking about the way the word is used in the sentence.

★ Clues about the meaning of an unknown word can be found by thinking about the facts and details in the paragraph where the word is found.

Read this Turkish folktale. As you read, ask yourself, "What clues will help me figure out the meaning of the word *maneuvered*?" Then answer the questions.

The Hoja

As he was journeying home on his donkey late one night, Nasreddin Hoja stopped at the village well to draw a drink for himself. He was horrified to see the full moon reflected in the dark water at the bottom of the well.

"The moon's fallen down the well," he muttered to himself. "I've got to rescue it. What would we do without the beautiful moon?"

Hoja grabbed the bucket and rope that lay beside the well and tossed the bucket in. Then he maneuvered it with the rope. He carefully moved the bucket about until it sat under the moon. Bending over the well, he tried to raise the bucket, but its lip was stuck on a stone. The more Hoja pulled, the less successful he was at raising the bucket and rescuing the moon. Finally, he braced his foot on the edge of the well and heaved. Suddenly, the bucket broke loose, and Hoja tumbled onto his back beside the well. Above him, he saw the lovely full moon floating serenely in the sky.

"Well, that's a good job done," he said to himself as he got to his feet. "Now the moon is back where it belongs!" And he went home to bed.

1. In paragraph three, the word *maneuvered* probably means
   Ⓐ "convinced someone to do something."
   Ⓑ "made a series of changes in movement."
   Ⓒ "pulled on a rope to lift something."
   Ⓓ "rescued something."

2. Which word gives a clue to the meaning of the word *maneuvered*?
   Ⓐ tossed
   Ⓑ braced
   Ⓒ moved
   Ⓓ heaved

Work with a partner. Talk about your answers to questions 1 and 2. Tell why you chose the answers you did.

Remember: The words and phrases around an unknown word often give clues about the word's meaning.

★ Look for context clues in the sentence where the word appears.
  Look also in the sentences before and after the unknown word.

★ Look for clues about the meaning of an unknown word by thinking about the way the word is used in the sentence.

★ Look for clues about the meaning of an unknown word by thinking about the facts and details in the paragraph where the word is found.

Read this poem about a forgetful boy. As you read, think about how you will figure out the meaning of any new words. Then answer the questions.

Godfrey Gordon Gustavus
by William Brighty Rands

Godfrey Gordon Gustavus Gore—
No doubt you have heard the name before—
Was a boy who never would shut a door!

The wind might whistle, the wind might roar,
And teeth be aching and throats be sore,
But still he never would shut the door.

His father would beg, his mother implore,
"Godfrey Gordon Gustavus Gore,
We really *do* wish you would shut the door!"

Their hands they wrung, their hair they tore;
But Godfrey Gordon Gustavus Gore
Was deaf as the buoy out at the Nore.

When he walked forth the folks would roar,
"Godfrey Gordon Gustavus Gore,
Why don't you think to shut the door?"

3. In stanza three, you can tell that the word *implore* means
   Ⓐ "argue."
   Ⓑ "excuse."
   Ⓒ "plead."
   Ⓓ "apologize."

4. Which word gives a clue to the meaning of the word *implore*?
   Ⓐ whistle
   Ⓑ wrung
   Ⓒ beg
   Ⓓ wish

FINDING WORD MEANING IN CONTEXT

Look at the answer choices for each question. Read why each answer choice is correct or not correct.

3. In stanza three, you can tell that the word *implore* means

   Ⓐ "argue."

   This answer is not correct because the poem suggests that the mother is frustrated more than she is angry.

   Ⓑ "excuse."

   This answer is not correct because the poem does not suggest that the mother is trying to excuse her son's behavior.

   ● "plead."

   This answer is correct because the words and phrases before and after the word tell about begging, wringing of hands, and tearing out of hair. You can figure out that the word implore *probably means "plead."*

   Ⓓ "apologize."

   This answer is not correct because the poem does not suggest that the mother feels any need to apologize for anything.

4. Which word gives a clue to the meaning of the word *implore*?

   Ⓐ whistle

   This answer is not correct because the word implore *is used to indicate that the mother is saying something. It is not likely that she is whistling her words.*

   Ⓑ wrung

   This answer is not correct because the word wrung *is what the parents did with their hands. Since the word* implore *comes just before a statement the mother makes,* wrung *cannot be the correct clue.*

   ● beg

   This answer is correct because the word beg *tells what the father did: the father begs, and the mother implores. It is logical to conclude that the words have the same meaning.*

   Ⓓ wish

   This answer is not correct because if you substitute the word wish *for the word* implore, *the statement that follows makes no sense.*

★ Look for a synonym, a word with a similar meaning, near an unknown word in a reading passage.

★ Look for an antonym, a word with an opposite meaning, near an unknown word in a reading passage.

★ Once you think you know the meaning of an unknown word, read the sentence where the word appears, using this new meaning. Does the sentence still make sense? If so, you've probably figured out the meaning of the word.

Read this history of the railroad. Then answer the questions.

During the mid-1800s, settlers and miners headed west in great numbers. Some traveled by covered wagon. Others sailed around the tip of South America. Both journeys were long and dangerous. Travelers wanted a faster and safer way to move west. In 1862, the United States passed a law to create a railroad that would stretch across the continent. The government offered land grants to two companies to build the new railroad. In 1863, the Central Pacific Railroad began laying tracks east from California. In 1864, the Union Pacific Railroad began laying tracks west from Nebraska.

At first, the two companies had trouble finding dependable workers, so the Union Pacific hired many immigrants from Europe. The Central Pacific recruited Chinese laborers. Many of the men had already settled in California during the gold rush in 1849.

Part of the railroad had to go through the Sierra Nevada. The Chinese workers had the hazardous task of blasting tunnels through the hard rock. Men were lowered down cliffs in straw baskets. Once lowered, they hammered holes into the rocky cliffs and put dynamite into the holes. Next, they lit the wicks of the dynamite. If the workers were lucky, they were pulled up to safe ground before the explosives went off.

In 1899, the Central Pacific track was finally linked to the Union Pacific track in Utah. The first transcontinental railroad was finally completed.

5. In paragraph two, which clue word is a synonym for *recruited?*
   - Ⓐ settled
   - Ⓒ hired
   - Ⓑ troubled
   - Ⓓ offered

6. In paragraph three, which clue word is an antonym for *hazardous?*
   - Ⓐ dangerous
   - Ⓒ rocky
   - Ⓑ safe
   - Ⓓ hard

7. In paragraph two, which word gives a clue to the meaning of *laborers?*
   - Ⓐ companies
   - Ⓒ men
   - Ⓑ workers
   - Ⓓ immigrants

8. In the last paragraph, the meaning of the word *transcontinental* is
   - Ⓐ "crossing a continent."
   - Ⓑ "crossing several continents."
   - Ⓒ "where two sets of tracks meet."
   - Ⓓ "from east to west."

Read this German fairy tale by the Brothers Grimm. Then answer the questions.

The Elves and the Shoemaker

There once was a shoemaker who had grown so poor that he had only enough leather to make one pair of shoes. One evening before bedtime, he cut out the leather so that he could begin working on the shoes early the next day. When he awoke the next morning, he was surprised to find a beautiful pair of new shoes already made. Soon a rich customer came in and bought the shoes. He paid the shoemaker so handsomely that the shoemaker was able to buy enough leather to make two new pairs of shoes. Again, in the evening, he cut out the leather. In the morning, he found the job already done. For the money he received from selling those two pairs, the shoemaker was able to buy enough leather to make four new pairs. On the third morning, the shoes were again already finished on his table. And so the nocturnal visits from the mysterious helper continued. As many shoes as the shoemaker cut out at night, that many were ready the following morning. Soon, the shoemaker was prosperous again.

One night, as the shoemaker was about to go to bed, he said to his wife, "Shouldn't we stay up just once to see who has been doing the work?"

So, the couple hid in the shop, and, around midnight, saw two elves appear, dressed in ragged clothes. The elves worked nimbly, and, in a flash, every shoe was made. Then, as quickly as they had arrived, the elves were gone.

The wife said to her husband, "These tiny men have made us rich. We must show our gratitude. The poor fellows must be cold in the rags they're wearing. Tomorrow, I will make them shirts, pants, coats, and stockings, and you make for each of them a tiny pair of shoes."

The following evening, the couple spread out the clothing. Then, eager to see how the elves would react, they hid themselves again and waited. Once more the elves came at midnight. When they saw the clothes, they quickly put them on. Then they began to hop and jump, and so they danced their way out of the door and never came back again.

9. In the first paragraph, you can tell that the word *handsomely* means
   Ⓐ "beautifully."
   Ⓑ "generously."
   Ⓒ "gratefully."
   Ⓓ "fairly."

10. In the first paragraph, which clue word is a synonym of *nocturnal*?
   Ⓐ night
   Ⓒ mysterious
   Ⓑ morning
   Ⓓ bedtime

11. In the first paragraph, which clue word is an antonym of *prosperous*?
   Ⓐ new
   Ⓒ rich
   Ⓑ surprised
   Ⓓ poor

12. In paragraph three, the best meaning of the word *nimbly* is
   Ⓐ "sleepily."
   Ⓑ "slowly and clumsily."
   Ⓒ "quickly and expertly."
   Ⓓ "sneakily."

★ A test question about finding meaning in context asks you about the meaning of a word from a reading passage. The word may or may not be familiar to you. The word might also be used in a new way.

★ A test question about finding meaning in context usually has several answer choices. If you have difficulty answering the question, try each answer choice in the sentence in which the word appears. Decide which answer choice makes the most sense in the reading passage.

Here is a poem about the building of city skyscrapers. Read the poem. Then do Numbers 13 and 14.

Song of the Builders
by Jessie Wilmore Murton

O beams of steel are slim and black
And danger lurks on the skyward track,
But men are many, and men are bold,
And what is risk, when the stake is gold?
  So riveters ring,
  And hot bolts fly,
  And strong men toil,
  And sweat . . . and die . . .
But the city's towers grow straight and high!
O beams of steel are black and slim,
But the wills of men are stubborn and grim,
They reach forever to clutch the sun,
And what is life, if the goal be won?
  So riveters ring,
  And hot bolts fly,
  And strong men toil,
  And sweat . . . and die . . .
But the city's towers grow straight and high!

Finding Word Meaning in Context

13. In line four, what is the best meaning of the word *stake*?
   Ⓐ "a pointed rod"
   Ⓑ "a reward or prize"
   Ⓒ "to claim as one's own"
   Ⓓ "a thick slice of beef"

Finding Word Meaning in Context

14. In line seven, you can tell that the word *toil* means
   Ⓐ "to charge a fee for a service."
   Ⓑ "to be lazy."
   Ⓒ "to be afraid."
   Ⓓ "to work hard."

Here is an article about an important medicine. Read the article.
Then do Numbers 15 and 16.

Victory over Smallpox

Smallpox was once one of the most dangerous diseases. It killed hundreds of millions of people throughout the world. Smallpox victims who got well again were often left blinded or badly scarred.

The first sign of smallpox was a high fever. A skin rash followed the fever. The rash then swelled up into watery spots. If the blisters began to bleed, the ill person soon died.

People who recovered from smallpox never got it again. Somehow, the first attack caused the body to defend itself against future attacks. For hundreds of years, doctors in Asia tried to protect healthy people against smallpox. Doctors would inject them with liquid taken from the blisters of smallpox victims. The procedure was risky, however. Usually the person got a mild case of the disease. But sometimes the person got a severe case of smallpox and died.

In 1796, a British physician named Edward Jenner improved on the Asian method. Jenner knew that men and women who milked cows often caught a disease called cowpox. Cowpox was similar to smallpox, but victims didn't get very ill from it. They just got a few skin blisters that soon went away. Some people believed that a person who had once had cowpox could not catch smallpox. Jenner tested this idea. He injected liquid from cowpox blisters into the arm of a young boy. The boy became mildly ill but recovered quickly. Later, Jenner injected

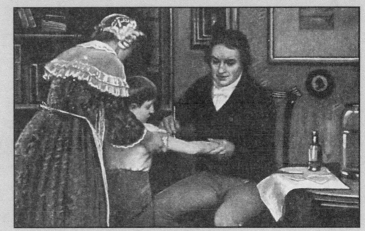

the boy with liquid from smallpox blisters. The boy did not become ill. Jenner repeated his experiment on other people many times with great success. He had created the first safe vaccine.

Finding Word Meaning in Context

15. In paragraph three, the word *inject* means
- Ⓐ "to put a fluid into the body with a needle."
- Ⓑ "to soak or drench."
- Ⓒ "to force to do something."
- Ⓓ "to add to a conversation."

Finding Word Meaning in Context

16. In paragraph four, the best meaning of the word *vaccine* is
- Ⓐ "a blister."
- Ⓑ "smallpox germs."
- Ⓒ "a medicine put into the body to protect a person from a disease."
- Ⓓ "a medicine used to clear up a rash."

STRATEGY 8

PART ONE: LEARN ABOUT DRAWING CONCLUSIONS AND MAKING INFERENCES

Read this fable from Aesop. As you read, try to figure out why the hunter was looking for the lion's tracks, but not for the lion himself.

The Hunter and the Woodcutter

A hunter was searching in the forest for signs of a lion. Before long, he caught sight of a woodcutter felling a tree. The hunter went up to the woodcutter and asked, "Excuse me, but have you noticed a lion's footprints anywhere about, or do you know where the lion's den might be?"

The woodcutter answered, "Come with me. I'll show you the lion himself."

The hunter turned pale, and his teeth chattered as he replied, "Oh, I'm not looking for the lion, thanks, only for his tracks."

The fable does not explain why the hunter was looking only for signs of the lion—and not the lion himself. It does, however, provide details that help you figure out why this happened.

The hunter turned pale, and his teeth chattered.

These details help you figure out that the hunter was afraid. You probably know from your own experiences that when people are scared, their skin may turn pale and their teeth may chatter.

Details are sometimes not clearly stated or explained in a reading passage. You must figure out some information on your own. Whenever you figure out something that is not told in a reading passage, you are **drawing a conclusion** or **making an inference**.

★ Pay attention to the details in a reading passage. You can use these details to figure out information that is not clearly stated or explained.

★ Use the details from the reading passage, as well as what you know from your own life, to draw a conclusion or to make an inference.

Read this poem by a Cuban-born poet. As you read, look for details that will help you figure out what the narrator is feeling. Then answer the questions.

Seeing Snow
by Gustavo Pérez Firmat

Had my father, my grandfather, and his,
had they been asked whether I would ever see snow,
they certainly—in another language—
would have answered,
no. Seeing snow for me
will always mean a slight or not so slight
suspension of the laws of nature.
I was not born to see snow.
I was not meant to see snow.
Even now, snowbound as I've been
all these years,
my surprise does not subside.
What, exactly, am I doing here?
Whose house is this anyway?
For sure one of us has strayed.
For sure someone's lost his way.
This must not be the place.
Where I come from, you know,
it's never snowed:
not once, not ever, not yet.

1. From the poem, you can tell that the narrator
   Ⓐ is tired of snow.
   Ⓑ will never see his homeland again.
   Ⓒ wishes that his ancestors had seen snow.
   Ⓓ wonders what he is doing in a land where it snows.

2. Which detail from the poem helped you answer question 1?
   Ⓐ "For sure one of us has strayed."
   Ⓑ "What, exactly, am I doing here?"
   Ⓒ "Where I come from, . . . it's never snowed: not once, not ever, not yet."
   Ⓓ "Even now, snowbound as I've been all these years, my surprise does not subside."

 Work with a partner. Talk about your answers to questions 1 and 2. Tell why you chose the answers you did.

Remember: Drawing a conclusion or making an inference is a way of figuring out information that is not stated in a reading passage.

★ Think about the details that are stated in a reading passage. Use these details to help you figure out information that is not explained.

★ Use the details from the reading passage and what you know from your own life to draw a conclusion or to make an inference.

Read this speech by Chief Joseph. As you read, ask yourself, "What details are explained? What information can I figure out on my own?" Then answer the questions.

In the 1860s, gold was discovered on Nez Percé land in the Northwest. The U.S. government tried to force the Nez Percé to move to reservations. A band of Nez Percé, led by Chief Joseph, resisted. Eventually, fighting broke out between the Nez Percé and the U.S. Army. Chief Joseph fled with his people to safety in Canada, but they were pursued. Just 40 miles from the border, soldiers attacked the Nez Percé camp. Here is a speech Chief Joseph gave after that attack:

October 5, 1877

I am tired of fighting. Our chiefs are killed. Looking Glass is dead. Toohulhulsote is dead. The old men are all dead. It is the young men who say yes or no. He who led the young men is dead. It is cold and we have no blankets. The little children are freezing to death. My people, some of them, have run away to the hills and have no blankets, no food. No one knows where they are—perhaps freezing to death. I want to have time to look for my children and see how many of them I can find. Maybe I shall find them among the dead. Hear me, my chiefs, I am tired. My heart is sick and sad. From where the sun now stands I will fight no more forever.

3. From the speech, what can you tell about Chief Joseph?

Ⓐ He was trying to convince the Nez Percé to stop fighting.

Ⓑ He was not a strong leader.

Ⓒ He was surrendering to the U.S. Army to prevent more deaths.

Ⓓ He feared for his life.

4. From what you have read, you can conclude that Chief Joseph

Ⓐ was angry that his people were suffering.

Ⓑ blamed himself that so many of his people had died.

Ⓒ was glad that his people had fought back.

Ⓓ was deeply concerned about his people.

Look at the answer choices for each question. Read why each answer choice is correct or not correct.

3. From the speech, what can you tell about Chief Joseph?

Ⓐ He was trying to convince the Nez Percé to stop fighting.

This answer is not correct because no details suggest that the Nez Percé had to be convinced to stop fighting. Many of the Nez Percé were dead or were hiding. Those that remained were hungry and cold, and had no strength to fight.

Ⓑ He was not a strong leader.

This answer is not correct because there is no reason to believe that Chief Joseph was not a strong leader. He never stopped caring about his people. He wanted to search for those who had run away to the hills.

● He was surrendering to the U.S. Army to prevent more deaths.

This answer is correct because details in the speech support Chief Joseph's statement that he is tired of fighting. He is saddened that so many of his people have died, and he just wants to end the killing.

Ⓓ He feared for his life.

This answer is not correct because there are no details in the speech to help you draw this conclusion. Chief Joseph seems to care more about saving his people's lives than his own life.

4. From what you read, you can conclude that Chief Joseph

Ⓐ was angry that his people were suffering.

This answer is not correct because no details help you draw the conclusion that Chief Joseph was angry. He says, "I am tired. My heart is sick and sad." These statements show that he has no anger in him now. He just wants the killing to end.

Ⓑ blamed himself that so many of his people had died.

This answer is not correct because no details indicate that Chief Joseph thought he was at fault for his people's deaths.

Ⓒ was glad that his people had fought back.

This answer is not correct because nothing in the speech suggests that this statement is true.

● was deeply concerned about his people.

This answer is correct because there is plenty of evidence to suggest that Chief Joseph was deeply concerned about his people. He was heartbroken about those who had died and worried about those who still lived.

★ Look for details in a reading passage that tell about how a person or character looks, acts, thinks, feels, and speaks. Think about what you know about people with similar qualities.

★ Look for details in a reading passage that suggest where or when something happens. If something happens at the Sears Tower, you can figure out that the setting is Chicago, Illinois. If something happens while the sun is shining, you can can figure out that it is daytime.

Read this article about some famous men. Then answer the questions.

When Thomas Edison was a boy, he asked a lot of questions. His schoolmaster labeled him "too stupid to learn." Consequently, Edison left school after only three months. Edison, though, was actually quite intelligent. He was an avid reader with a curious mind. Edison's curiosity led him to become a great inventor. With the help of his staff, he created over 1,000 inventions. He is most famous for inventing the electric light bulb.

Winston Churchill also did poorly in school. Although he was judged to have no promise, Churchill grew up to become a great man. Churchill served as prime minister of Great Britain during World War II. His leadership strengthened the spirits of his countrymen as the Germans bombed British cities. Churchill wrote a six-book history of the war. This effort won him the Nobel Prize in Literature in 1953. That same year, he was also knighted "sir."

Young Albert Einstein was a slow learner. He did not talk until he was four and did not read until he was nine. No one suspected that he would be one of the most famous scientists in the world. Dr. Einstein's theories changed the way people viewed the world. In 1921, this genius won the Nobel Prize in Physics.

5. From the article, you can tell that Edison
   Ⓐ took credit for other people's inventions.
   Ⓑ wished that he had stayed in school.
   Ⓒ asked so many questions as a boy because he was curious, not stupid.
   Ⓓ was smarter than most of his teachers.

6. Details in the article suggest that Churchill
   Ⓐ became a gifted writer as well as leader.
   Ⓑ was supportive of the war.
   Ⓒ liked being called "sir."
   Ⓓ left school when he was very young.

7. There is enough information in the article to show that Einstein
   Ⓐ began forming physics theories during his childhood.
   Ⓑ was not a genius as a boy.
   Ⓒ never went to college.
   Ⓓ never wanted to be famous.

8. From the article, what can you conclude about all three men?
   Ⓐ They all won a Nobel Prize.
   Ⓑ They were all lazy as boys.
   Ⓒ They were all geniuses.
   Ⓓ They were successful people who were unsuccessful in school.

Read this humorous story from Great Britain. Then answer the questions.

Master of All Masters

A girl once went in search of a position as a maid. At last, an old gentleman hired her. On the girl's first day of work, the man firmly explained that in his house he had his own names for things.

He said to her, "What will you call me?"

"Master or mister, or whatever you please, sir," the girl answered.

"No, you must call me 'master of all masters,'" the man said. Pointing to his bed, he asked, "And what would you call this?"

"Bed or bunk, or whatever you please, sir."

"No, that's my 'barnacle.'" Pointing to his trousers, he said, "And what do you call these?"

"Pants or trousers, or whatever you please, sir."

"You must call them 'squibs and crackers.'" Pointing to his cat, he asked, "And what would you call her?"

"Cat or Kitty, or whatever you please, sir."

"You must call her 'white-faced simminy.'" Pointing at the fire, he demanded, "And what would you call this?"

"Fire or flame, or whatever you please, sir."

"You must call it 'hot cockalorum.'" He went on, pointing to the water. "And what is this?"

"Water or wet, or whatever you please, sir."

"No, 'pondalorum' is its name. And what do you call all this?" asked the man as he gestured toward his entire home.

"House or cottage, or whatever you please, sir."

"You must call it 'high topper mountain.'"

That night, the maid woke her master up in a fright. "Master of all masters," she shouted, "get out of your barnacle and put on your squibs and crackers. For white-faced simminy has got a spark of hot cockalorum on its tail, and unless you get some pondalorum, high topper mountain will be all on hot cockalorum."

9. From the story, you can tell that the girl
   Ⓐ did not respect the man.
   Ⓑ was frightened by the man's behavior.
   Ⓒ was an obedient maid.
   Ⓓ had poor hearing.

10. Details in the story suggest that the man
   Ⓐ is quite peculiar.
   Ⓑ has never had a maid before.
   Ⓒ likes to play games.
   Ⓓ does not speak English very well.

11. What can you conclude about the cat?
   Ⓐ It was an orange cat.
   Ⓑ It had gotten too close to the fire.
   Ⓒ It was jealous of the girl.
   Ⓓ It liked to sleep on the man's bed.

12. There is enough information in the story to show that
   Ⓐ the man will consider using the real names for things.
   Ⓑ the man will fire his new maid.
   Ⓒ the girl will learn more unusual names.
   Ⓓ the man's house will be destroyed.

★ A test question about drawing conclusions or making inferences asks you to figure out something that is not stated in a reading passage.

★ A test question about drawing conclusions or making inferences often contains the words *you can tell, determine,* or *conclude.*

Here is an article from a math Web site. Read the article. Then do Numbers 13 and 14.

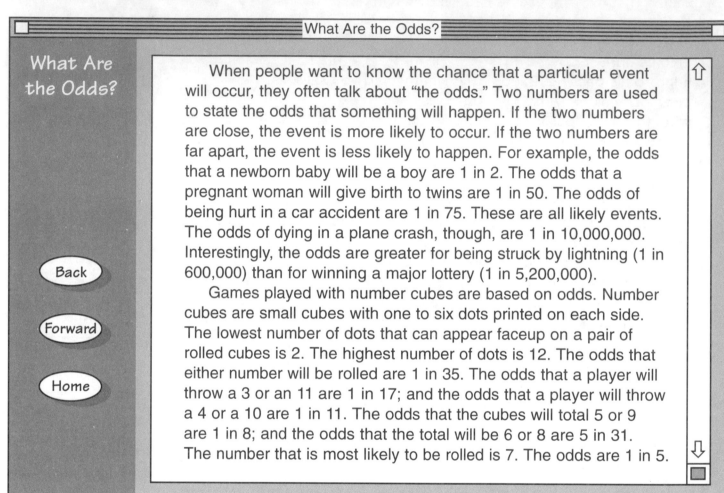

What Are the Odds?

What Are the Odds?

Back

Forward

Home

When people want to know the chance that a particular event will occur, they often talk about "the odds." Two numbers are used to state the odds that something will happen. If the two numbers are close, the event is more likely to occur. If the two numbers are far apart, the event is less likely to happen. For example, the odds that a newborn baby will be a boy are 1 in 2. The odds that a pregnant woman will give birth to twins are 1 in 50. The odds of being hurt in a car accident are 1 in 75. These are all likely events. The odds of dying in a plane crash, though, are 1 in 10,000,000. Interestingly, the odds are greater for being struck by lightning (1 in 600,000) than for winning a major lottery (1 in 5,200,000).

Games played with number cubes are based on odds. Number cubes are small cubes with one to six dots printed on each side. The lowest number of dots that can appear faceup on a pair of rolled cubes is 2. The highest number of dots is 12. The odds that either number will be rolled are 1 in 35. The odds that a player will throw a 3 or an 11 are 1 in 17; and the odds that a player will throw a 4 or a 10 are 1 in 11. The odds that the cubes will total 5 or 9 are 1 in 8; and the odds that the total will be 6 or 8 are 5 in 31. The number that is most likely to be rolled is 7. The odds are 1 in 5.

Drawing Conclusions and Making Inferences

13. There is enough information in the article to show that
   Ⓐ a newborn baby is more likely to be a girl than a boy.
   Ⓑ dying in a plane crash is an unlikely event.
   Ⓒ a person is more likely to win a lottery than to be struck by lightning.
   Ⓓ a person is more likely to be in a plane crash than to win a lottery.

Drawing Conclusions and Making Inferences

14. From the article, you can conclude that the odds are greater
   Ⓐ for rolling a 2 than a 3.
   Ⓑ for rolling a 4 than a 5.
   Ⓒ for rolling a 7 than a 9.
   Ⓓ for rolling a 6 than an 8.

Here is a story about a popular character in Arab folktales. Read the folktale. Then do Numbers 15 and 16.

Djuba's Guests

Djuba had a good friend who was a hunter. One day, the hunter visited Djuba in the city and brought him a nice fat hare as a present. Djuba roasted the hare and invited the hunter to stay and share it with him.

The next day, a man knocked at Djuba's door. Djuba opened the door and saw a stranger at his doorstep. "I'm sorry," Djuba told the man, "but I do not recognize you. May I ask who you are?"

The stranger smiled and replied, "Why, I am a friend of your good friend the hunter, who brought you the nice fat hare."

Now, the rules of hospitality required that Djuba invite this friend-of-a-friend in for a meal. But as the two men talked over dinner, Djuba realized that the stranger didn't really know the hunter very well at all. The man had only been after a free meal. Djuba was not happy, but he couldn't just throw a guest out of his house. He just smiled most hospitably and waited for the stranger to leave.

Djuba thought about his situation. "Now I have a reputation as an easy source for a free meal," he told himself. "I don't mind giving charity to the truly needy, but I do object to feeding every thief that appears at my door. How can I stop these crooks without being rude?" Djuba pondered this question for a while, and, at last, he came up with a solution.

The next day, as expected, another stranger arrived at Djuba's door. "And who are you?" Djuba asked the man.

"Why, I am the friend of the friend of your good friend the hunter, who brought you the nice fat hare!"

"Welcome," Djuba told the man. "Come inside and join me for a meal."

Djuba placed a steaming bowl of hot water on the table. The stranger looked at the bowl with a puzzled frown. "What is this?" he asked.

Djuba smiled. "Why, this is the water that was boiled in the very same pot as the nice fat hare that my good friend the hunter, whose friend you know, brought me!"

Drawing Conclusions and Making Inferences

15. From the folktale, you can tell that Djuba
    - Ⓐ does not like strangers.
    - Ⓑ does not trust most people.
    - Ⓒ is not very generous.
    - Ⓓ is very clever.

Drawing Conclusions and Making Inferences

16. From the folktale, you can conclude that
    - Ⓐ no more strangers appeared at Djuba's door.
    - Ⓑ Djuba and the hunter stopped being friends.
    - Ⓒ Djuba never invited another person into his home for a meal.
    - Ⓓ Djuba began offering meals to the truly needy.

PART ONE: LEARN ABOUT DISTINGUISHING BETWEEN FACT AND OPINION

Read this poster for a school election. As you read, look for statements that can be proved. Also look for statements that tell what someone thinks or feels.

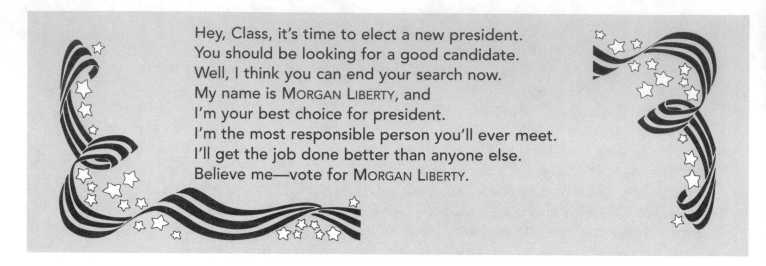

Hey, Class, it's time to elect a new president.
You should be looking for a good candidate.
Well, I think you can end your search now.
My name is MORGAN LIBERTY, and
I'm your best choice for president.
I'm the most responsible person you'll ever meet.
I'll get the job done better than anyone else.
Believe me—vote for MORGAN LIBERTY.

The statements that can be proved are

Hey, Class, it's time to elect a new president.

You should be looking for a good candidate.

My name is Morgan Liberty.

The statements that tell what someone thinks or feels are

Well, I think you can end your search now.

I'm your best choice for president.

I'm the most responsible person you'll ever meet.

I'll get the job done better than anyone else.

Believe me—vote for Morgan Liberty.

If a statement can be proved, it is a **fact**. If a statement tells what someone thinks or feels about something, it is an **opinion**. Facts can be proved. Opinions cannot. When you figure out if a statement is a fact or an opinion, you are **distinguishing between fact and opinion**.

★ Facts are statements that can be checked or proved.

★ Opinions are statements that cannot be proved. They tell what someone thinks or feels.

★ Opinions often contain clue words such as *think, feel, believe,* and *seem*. Other common clue words are *always, never, all, none, most, least, greatest, best,* and *worst*.

Read this friendly letter. As you read, ask yourself, "Which statements can be proved? Which statements cannot be proved?" Then answer the questions.

> 1489 Park Street
> Alexandria, VA 22301
> October 10, 2000
>
> Dear Sela,
>
> Let me tell you about my teacher this year. Her name is Ms. Lightfoot, and she's the most extraordinary teacher in the world. Ms. Lightfoot is so kind, funny, and patient that it's impossible not to like her. I also think she must be the smartest person to have ever taught in my school. She knows how to make every subject interesting, even geography! But she doesn't only teach us academic things. She also teaches us the importance of honesty, loyalty, kindness, and respect. She constantly reminds us to be true to ourselves and fair to others. She is the greatest human being.
>
> All the kids in my class think Ms. Lightfoot is cool. She dresses in the latest fashions, and she never has a bad hair day. She's always up-to-date on pop culture. Every morning, before the bell rings, she asks us trivia questions about recent TV shows, new movies, and hit songs. I'm getting pretty good at the game.
>
> I hope you like your new teacher as much as I like Ms. Lightfoot. (However, that doesn't seem likely!) Write back and let me know.
>
> Your friend,
> Felicity

1. Which of these statements tells a fact about Ms. Lightfoot?

   Ⓐ She is the greatest human being.

   Ⓑ She is Felicity's teacher.

   Ⓒ She is the most extraordinary teacher in the world.

   Ⓓ She is loved by everyone.

2. Which clue word signals an opinion about Ms. Lightfoot's intelligence?

   Ⓐ think

   Ⓑ seem

   Ⓒ best

   Ⓓ believe

Work with a partner. Talk about your answers to questions 1 and 2. Tell why you chose the answers you did.

Remember: Facts can be proved. Opinions cannot be proved.

★ To find out if a statement is a fact, ask yourself, "Can this statement be checked or proved?"

★ To find out if a statement is an opinion, ask yourself, "Does this statement tell what someone thinks or feels?"

★ Look for clue words that signal an opinion, such as *think, feel, believe, seem, always, never, all, none, most, least, greatest, best,* and *worst.*

Read this article about an unusual bird. As you read, think about which statements are facts and which statements are opinions. Then answer the questions.

Bobo, the Clown

The blue-footed booby is probably the goofiest bird on the planet. With its bright-blue webbed feet, the seabird looks like a clown. The name *booby* comes from the Spanish word *bobo*, which means "stupid fellow." Sailors called the birds "boobies" because the animals move clumsily on land and are very tame. The birds would sit perfectly still as sailors walked up to them and picked them up. They didn't have enough sense to be afraid.

The male booby performs the silliest mating rituals to attract a female. He displays his blue feet in an exaggerated high-stepping dance. If the female is interested, she will join the dance. After a flight over his territory, the courting male will also wave his feet at the female just before he lands. He seems to be saluting her.

In the air, the blue-footed booby is the most graceful flyer. The birds spend much of their time gliding over water, watching the surface for food. When a bird spots a fish, it signals the other boobies in the flock with a single whistle. Then they follow the leader as it plunges into the water. Boobies are also the best divers. The birds can dive from heights up to 80 feet. With their bill pointed downward and their wings angled close to their body, they drop downward at great speed. When they hit the water, there is barely a splash.

3. Which of these statements about the blue-footed booby can be proved?
   Ⓐ It is the most graceful flyer.
   Ⓑ It is the goofiest bird on the planet.
   Ⓒ It is the best diver.
   Ⓓ It can dive from 80 feet high.

4. Which of these statements tells what the writer thinks or feels?
   Ⓐ The booby is very tame.
   Ⓑ The booby spends much of its time gliding over water.
   Ⓒ The male booby performs the silliest mating rituals.
   Ⓓ *Booby* comes from a word meaning "stupid fellow."

Look at the answer choices for each question. Read why each answer choice is correct or not correct.

3. Which of these statements about the blue-footed booby can be proved?

Ⓐ It is the most graceful flyer.

This answer is not correct because it cannot be proved from the facts in the article. The blue-footed booby may be a graceful flyer, but another bird may be just as graceful, if not more.

Ⓑ It is the goofiest bird on the planet.

This answer is not correct because it cannot be proved. The blue-footed booby may look and act goofy to the writer, but others may feel differently about the bird's looks and actions.

Ⓒ It is the best diver.

This answer is not correct because it cannot be proved from the facts given. Boobies are good divers, but some other creature may be just as good, if not better.

● It can dive from 80 feet high.

This answer is correct because you can prove that this statement is true. You can observe the bird, or you can find facts about the bird in a book, on a CD-ROM encyclopedia, or on the Internet.

4. Which of these statements tells what the writer thinks or feels?

Ⓐ The booby is very tame.

This answer is not correct because this statement is a fact, not an opinion. Proof is provided in the description of the blue-footed boobies that sat perfectly still as sailors walked up to them and picked them up. The birds were not afraid. You can check this fact in a book, on a CD-ROM encyclopedia, or on the Internet.

Ⓑ The booby spends much of its time gliding over water.

This answer is not correct because it can be proved. You can observe the bird, or you can find facts about the bird in a book, on a CD-ROM encyclopedia, or on the Internet.

● The male booby performs the silliest mating rituals.

This answer is correct because the statement cannot be proved. The statement is the writer's opinion about the male booby's behavior during mating season. A scientist who studies animal behavior may not think these rituals are silly at all.

Ⓓ *Booby* comes from a word meaning "stupid fellow."

This answer is not correct because the statement can be proved. The article states that the word booby *comes from the Spanish word* bobo, *which means "stupid fellow." You can find this fact in a book about the bird, on a CD-ROM encyclopedia, or on the Internet.*

★ Facts can be observed, checked, or tested. You can prove that a fact is correct or true.

★ Opinions express someone's thoughts, feelings, or beliefs. An opinion can be about an event, an idea, a person, or a thing. Even though a person might agree or disagree with an opinion, it still cannot be proved.

Read this report written by Roberto. Then answer the questions.

A Tribute to a Hero

Roberto Clemente was the finest athlete to grace the sport of baseball. I'm proud to be named in his memory. He is a hero to all Latinos, like me.

Clemente was born in Carolina, Puerto Rico, in 1934. He began playing for the Pittsburgh Pirates in 1955. Clemente had a back injury from a 1954 car accident, so he often played in great pain. Still, he always gave his team his best effort. Clemente had a strong throwing arm and was an excellent batter. He helped the Pirates win the World Series twice (in 1960 and in 1971). In 1966, Clemente won the Most Valuable Player award. In 1972, he made his 3,000th hit. Only ten other men in baseball history had achieved that many hits.

Clemente was not just a great baseball player; he was also the world's most generous man. Every winter, he returned to Puerto Rico to teach baseball to the island's youth. He also planned the building of a sports center for them. When an earthquake struck Nicaragua, in 1972, Clemente collected supplies for the victims. Then he rented a cargo plane to deliver the supplies. Shortly after taking off, the plane crashed into the ocean, and Clemente was drowned.

All sports fans mourned his death. Within three months, Clemente was elected into the National Baseball Hall of Fame. He was the first Latino to earn this honor.

5. Which of these statements about Clemente cannot be proved?
   Ⓐ He made 3,000 hits.
   Ⓑ He played for the Pirates.
   Ⓒ He is a hero to all Latinos.
   Ⓓ He was a Most Valuable Player.

6. Which of these statements is an opinion about Clemente?
   Ⓐ He was the finest athlete to grace the sport of baseball.
   Ⓑ He had a strong throwing arm.
   Ⓒ Every winter, he returned to Puerto Rico.
   Ⓓ He helped the Pirates win the World Series twice.

7. Which of these clue words signals an opinion about Clemente's generosity?
   Ⓐ more
   Ⓑ most
   Ⓒ always
   Ⓓ never

8. Which is a fact about Clemente that can be proved?
   Ⓐ He always gave his best effort.
   Ⓑ He was the world's most generous man.
   Ⓒ He was the first Latino elected into the Baseball Hall of Fame.
   Ⓓ All sports fans mourned his death.

Read this courtroom conversation. Then answer the questions.

DOG—Your Honor, I'm here to complain about Porcupine's behavior. I believe that he's a danger to society.

PORCUPINE—A danger? Why, I've never done anything wrong in my life!

DOG—Is that a fact? Then how do you explain these quills I'm wearing?

JUDGE—Yes, Porcupine, how did those quills get stuck in Dog's skin?

PORCUPINE—Your Honor, it seems to me that Dog was at fault for his injury. He's wearing my quills because he got too close to me.

DOG—You tell the biggest fibs! You know that you shot your quills at me.

PORCUPINE—You're always making ridiculous statements. Everyone knows that porcupines can't shoot their quills.

JUDGE—He's right, Dog. I think you owe Porcupine an apology.

DOG—But, Judge, Porcupine still caused me harm. When he spotted me in the woods last night, his quills stood straight up, like pins in a pincushion. Then he turned his back to me and shook his tail. The next thing I knew, his sharp quills were piercing my skin. Believe me, the pain is worse than anything anyone has ever felt.

PORCUPINE—Oh, stop whining, Dog. You're always complaining.

JUDGE—Porcupine, did you use your quills as weapons?

PORCUPINE—Not exactly, Your Honor. Dog didn't tell you why I bumped into him. I was afraid because he had threatened me. And when I'm frightened, my quills stand straight up and come loose easily.

JUDGE—So, Dog, what do you have to say for yourself?

And for once, Dog had nothing to say.

9. Which of these statements about Porcupine can be proved?
   Ⓐ He's a danger to society.
   Ⓑ His quills stand up straight when he's frightened.
   Ⓒ He's never done anything wrong in his life.
   Ⓓ He tells the biggest fibs.

10. Which of these statements is a fact about Dog?
   Ⓐ He is at fault for his injury.
   Ⓑ He is always complaining.
   Ⓒ He is always making ridiculous statements.
   Ⓓ He was hurt by Porcupine's quills.

11. Which of these statements is an opinion from the passage?
   Ⓐ Porcupine backed into Dog because he was afraid.
   Ⓑ Dog admitted that he might have growled at Porcupine.
   Ⓒ Everyone knows that porcupines can't shoot their quills.
   Ⓓ Dog didn't touch Porcupine.

12. Which of these statements cannot be proved?
   Ⓐ Dog's pain is worse than anything anyone has ever felt.
   Ⓑ Porcupine's quills come loose easily when he is frightened.
   Ⓒ Dog didn't tell all the facts at first.
   Ⓓ Porcupine and Dog met in the woods.

★ A test question about distinguishing between fact and opinion may ask you to identify which of four statements is a fact or an opinion.

★ To recognize a fact, read each answer choice, and ask yourself, "Can this statement be proved?" If it can, then it is a fact.

★ To recognize an opinion, read each answer choice, and ask yourself, "Does this statement tell what someone thinks or feels?" If it does, then it is an opinion. Also, look for clue words in the answer choices that signal an opinion.

**Here is a journal entry by Peter. Read the journal entry.
Then do Numbers 13 and 14.**

May 14, 2000

I'm tired of being treated like a child in my family. Even though my brother is only two years older than I am, my parents act as if I'm a lot younger. It seems to me that my brother always gets to do whatever he wants to do. Stephen stays up late at night. I have to go to bed by 9:00 P.M. Stephen goes to all the latest movies. Every time I want to go with him, my parents say that I'm not old enough. My brother can also ride his bike anywhere in town. I'm allowed only to ride back and forth to school— and it's only four blocks away. I never get to go anywhere alone. Stephen goes many places by himself.

Besides having all kinds of freedom (when I have none), Stephen also gets a bigger allowance than I do. I think that by giving me less spending money, my parents are making certain that I can't afford to do anything on my own. Every time I complain to my parents that they treat Stephen and I differently, they say the same thing. They tell me, "When you're older, you'll get to have these privileges too."

The worst insult, however, is that Stephen bosses me around all the time. "Do this, Peter. Do that, Peter." I'm sick of it. The Constitution of the United States says that all men are created equally. So why don't these rules apply to younger brothers?

Distinguishing Between Fact and Opinion

13. Which of these is an opinion from the journal entry?

- Ⓐ Stephen is only two years older than Peter.
- Ⓑ Stephen always gets to do whatever he wants to do.
- Ⓒ Stephen stays up late at night.
- Ⓓ Stephen goes many places by himself.

Distinguishing Between Fact and Opinion

14. Which of these is a fact from the journal entry?

- Ⓐ Peter has no freedom.
- Ⓑ Every time Peter wants to see a film, he's told he's not old enough.
- Ⓒ Stephen gets a bigger allowance than Peter.
- Ⓓ Stephen bosses Peter around all the time.

Here is a student's book report. Read the book report.
Then do Numbers 15 and 16.

I just read the most exciting book ever written. It has everything I like in a book—humor, adventure, romance, and magic. The book is a huge collection of ancient folktales from Arabia, India, and Persia. It's called *Arabian Nights.*

The book begins with the story of a king who was betrayed by his queen. The king was so bitter that he vowed to marry a new maiden each night. The next morning, he would have her beheaded. One bride, named Scheherazade, however, was more clever than all the others. She delayed having her head chopped off by telling her new husband a story. The king was so delighted by his bride's tale that he allowed her to live another day to finish it. Scheherazade wove one tale after another for a thousand and one nights. In this way, she saved her life and won the king's love.

Three of the most popular tales from *Arabian Nights* are "Aladdin," "Sinbad the Sailor," and "Ali Baba and the Forty Thieves." I thought "Aladdin" was the best story. It is about a poor, but idle, boy named Aladdin. One day, he meets a cunning magician, who claims to be his uncle. The magician tricks Aladdin into entering an underground cave to recover an old lamp. When Aladdin returns to the mouth of the cave with the lamp, the magician demands that he hand it over immediately. But Aladdin refuses to give up the lamp until he is out of the cave safely. The magician flies into a rage and traps Aladdin in the dark cave. By accident, Aladdin discovers that when the lamp is rubbed, an enormous genie appears. The genie promises to obey Aladdin in all ways. With the genie's help, Aladdin eventually gains wealth and power. He also wins the hand of a sultan's beautiful daughter.

Arabian Nights has about 200 stories and took me forever to read. I was sad, though, when the stories finally ended. No other book could provide more reading enjoyment.

Distinguishing Between Fact and Opinion

15. Which of these is a fact about *Arabian Nights?*
    Ⓐ It is the most exciting book ever written.
    Ⓑ No other book could provide more reading enjoyment.
    Ⓒ It took forever to read.
    Ⓓ It is a collection of ancient folktales.

Distinguishing Between Fact and Opinion

16. Which of these is an opinion from the book report?
    Ⓐ "Aladdin" is the best story in *Arabian Nights.*
    Ⓑ Scheherazade wove tales to save her life.
    Ⓒ "Sinbad the Sailor" is one tale from *Arabian Nights.*
    Ⓓ *Arabian Nights* has humor, adventure, romance, and magic.

REVIEW STRATEGIES 7–9

PART ONE: READ A JOURNAL ENTRY

Here is a journal entry from the crew member of a cruise ship. Read the journal entry. Then do Numbers 1 through 6.

Monday, December 5

The <u>Sea Rover</u> has just left the island of Bermuda. It will be traveling south to Puerto Rico. Then, on Friday, the ship will turn west and head back to Miami. This route takes us through the most dreaded area in the Atlantic Ocean. We will have to pass through the Bermuda Triangle!

The Bermuda Triangle got its name after an event that occurred in 1945. On December 5, five United States Navy planes vanished while flying over the region. No one knows how or why this happened. After one of the largest searches in history, no wreckage was ever found—not until May 1991, that is. Finally, the five missing planes were recovered just 10 miles off the Florida coast.

Since 1945, more than one hundred ships and planes are believed to have vanished in the Bermuda Triangle. For this reason, the region is also known as the Devil's Triangle, Atlantic's Graveyard, and the Twilight Zone.

Books and TV shows have provided many explanations for the mysterious disappearances. Some people blame undersea earthquakes. They say that the earthquakes churned up gargantuan waves that swallowed up the vessels. Others believe that the missing boats and planes entered time warps and were sent into the past or the future. A few people claim that aliens were responsible for the missing vessels.

Most disappearances at sea are probably caused by bad weather, broken equipment, or human error. Accidents can happen at sea. There are just as many losses in other parts of the ocean as in the Bermuda Triangle. The ocean is vast and deep. It's not surprising that some vessels are never recovered.

Finding Word Meaning in Context

1. In the first paragraph, the name
   Sea Rover probably means
   Ⓐ "a sea dog or sailor."
   Ⓑ "something that roams the sea."
   Ⓒ "a boat that is propelled by oars."
   Ⓓ "a ship that is lost at sea."

Finding Word Meaning in Context

2. In paragraph four, the best meaning of
   the word *gargantuan* is
   Ⓐ "tiny."
   Ⓑ "huge."
   Ⓒ "smooth."
   Ⓓ "graceful."

Drawing Conclusions and Making Inferences

3. There is enough information in the
   journal entry to show that
   Ⓐ most disappearances in the Bermuda
   Triangle can be explained.
   Ⓑ there is no such thing as the Bermuda
   Triangle.
   Ⓒ most pilots and ship captains avoid
   the Bermuda Triangle.
   Ⓓ crossing the ocean by ship or boat
   is perfectly safe.

Drawing Conclusions and Making Inferences

4. From the journal entry, you can tell that
   the crew member
   Ⓐ doesn't believe that the disappearances
   were ordinary accidents.
   Ⓑ likes to solve mysteries.
   Ⓒ is trying to understand the mystery of
   the Bermuda Triangle.
   Ⓓ is thrilled to be traveling through
   the Bermuda Triangle.

Distinguishing Between Fact and Opinion

5. Which of these is an opinion from
   the journal entry?
   Ⓐ Books provide many explanations
   for the disappearances.
   Ⓑ Accidents can happen at sea.
   Ⓒ In 1945, five navy planes were lost
   in the Bermuda Triangle.
   Ⓓ The Bermuda Triangle is the most
   dreaded area in the Atlantic Ocean.

Distinguishing Between Fact and Opinion

6. Which of these is a fact?
   Ⓐ More should be done to understand
   the Bermuda Triangle.
   Ⓑ Undersea earthquakes are
   amazing events.
   Ⓒ The Bermuda Triangle is also called
   Atlantic's Graveyard.
   Ⓓ Only foolish people believe in
   time warps.

Here is a short biography of a famous president. Read the biography.
Then do Numbers 7 through 12.

Did you know that the popular teddy bear was named for President Theodore ("Teddy") Roosevelt? He was the 26th president of the United States. It is said that, while hunting in Mississippi, a small bear cub was brought to President Roosevelt to shoot. But he refused, believing that the animal did not have a chance to defend itself. The story of his tender deed quickly spread, and soon the country was flooded with stuffed bear cubs, or teddy bears.

Roosevelt was born in 1858 to a wealthy family from New York City. As a child, he was often sick. As he grew, he made himself stronger by exercising. In time, Roosevelt became quite a sportsman. He was a good boxer, horseman, rower, tennis player, and hunter.

Roosevelt had many careers. He was a writer, a rancher, and a lawyer. In politics, he served as a police commissioner, a governor, a vice president, and, of course, president. He was also a national war hero. In 1898, Roosevelt served as a colonel in the Spanish-American War. The United States fought in this war to help Cuba win its freedom from Spain. Roosevelt formed a regiment of horsemen known as the Rough Riders. His bravery during battle led to his rise in politics. In 1898, he was elected governor of New York. In March 1901, he became President William McKinley's vice president. When McKinley was killed six months later, Roosevelt became president. He was the youngest man ever to become president. He was only 42.

President Roosevelt never rested. He helped to pass important laws. He forced companies to give workers higher wages and improve working conditions. He took steps to protect our country's wilderness. He set aside tracts of land as national parks and forests. He supported the building of the Panama Canal to make it easier for ships to travel between the Atlantic and the Pacific. In 1906, he won the Nobel Peace Prize for helping to end a war between Russia and Japan. He was the first American president to win a Nobel Prize. He was also the first president to ride in a car, fly in an airplane, and travel in a submarine.

Despite his busy schedule, Roosevelt always made time for his six children. He told them stories and played games. Together, they wrestled, played hide-and-seek, and had wild pillow fights.

Theodore Roosevelt died in 1919, at age 60. But every American still remembers the man with the big heart. A likeness of his face is carved at Mount Rushmore, in South Dakota.

Finding Word Meaning in Context

7. In paragraph three, the word *regiment* means

    Ⓐ "a daily diet."

    Ⓑ "a special routine."

    Ⓒ "a military unit."

    Ⓓ "to put in order."

Finding Word Meaning in Context

8. In paragraph four, you can tell that the word *tracts* means

    Ⓐ "paths or trails."

    Ⓑ "where trains run."

    Ⓒ "small spaces."

    Ⓓ "large areas."

Drawing Conclusions and Making Inferences

9. There is enough information in the biography to show that Roosevelt

    Ⓐ was an adventurous man.

    Ⓑ was a stern colonel.

    Ⓒ was known to behave foolishly.

    Ⓓ was a devoted husband.

Drawing Conclusions and Making Inferences

10. From the biography, you can tell that Roosevelt

    Ⓐ loved the West.

    Ⓑ had a great sense of humor.

    Ⓒ owned many teddy bears.

    Ⓓ had a lot of energy.

Distinguishing Between Fact and Opinion

11. Which of these is an opinion from the biography?

    Ⓐ Roosevelt was the first president to win a Nobel Prize.

    Ⓑ Roosevelt had many careers.

    Ⓒ Roosevelt never rested.

    Ⓓ Roosevelt was the youngest person to become president.

Distinguishing Between Fact and Opinion

12. Which of these is a fact?

    Ⓐ Everyone has heard of teddy bears.

    Ⓑ The teddy bear was named for "Teddy" Roosevelt.

    Ⓒ Roosevelt was the most wonderful and caring of fathers.

    Ⓓ All Americans admired Roosevelt.

PART ONE: LEARN ABOUT IDENTIFYING AUTHOR'S PURPOSE

Read this Chinese folktale. As you read, think about why the author probably wrote the folktale.

Holding Up the Sky

One day, an elephant saw a hummingbird lying flat on its back on the ground. The bird's tiny feet were raised up in the air.

"What on earth are you doing, Hummingbird?" asked the elephant.

The hummingbird replied, "I have heard that the sky might fall today. If that should happen, I am ready to do my bit in holding it up."

The elephant laughed and mocked the tiny bird. "Do you think THOSE little feet could hold up the SKY?"

"Not alone," admitted the hummingbird. "But each must do what he can. And this is what *I* can do."

From *Peace Tales: World Folktales to Talk About*
by Margaret Read MacDonald

The author probably wrote the folktale to make readers laugh or smile. The author's purpose is to entertain readers with a folktale that teaches a lesson.

All authors write for a reason. The reason an author writes something is called the author's purpose. When you figure out why a reading passage was written, you are **identifying the author's purpose**. Authors write for one of four reasons—to describe, to entertain, to explain, or to persuade.

★ If a reading passage contains many details about a person, place, or thing, the author's purpose is to **describe**.

★ If a reading passage is enjoyable to read, tells a personal story, or uses a story to teach a lesson, the author's purpose is to **entertain**.

★ If a reading passage provides facts about a particular subject or tells readers how to do something, the author's purpose is to **explain**.

★ If a reading passage tries to get readers to do something, buy something, or believe something, the author's purpose is to **persuade**.

Read this newspaper article written about Thanksgiving Day. As you read, try to figure out the author's purpose for writing the article. Then answer the questions.

Thanksgiving Myths
by I. M. Agobbler

For nearly one hundred years, Thanksgiving Day has been celebrated in November. No one really knows, though, when the first Thanksgiving took place. Records show only that it occurred sometime in the autumn of 1621. The early Thanksgivings didn't occur each year. And they didn't always happen in the fall. In 1623, for example, Thanksgiving was celebrated in July.

Today, turkey is the most popular choice for Thanksgiving dinner. However, turkey wasn't served at the first Thanksgiving. In fact, there probably wasn't a turkey within miles of the feast. The Pilgrims and their Native American guests fed mostly on deer, duck, goose, and seafood. They also ate cornbread, vegetables, and fruits.

Thanksgiving was popular mainly with New Englanders for its first two hundred years. In 1827, Sarah Josepha Hale began a campaign to make Thanksgiving a national holiday. Finally, in 1863, President Lincoln set aside the last Thursday of November as the official holiday.

In 1939, President Roosevelt moved Thanksgiving to the third Thursday of November. The change occurred so that there would be more shopping days for Christmas. Many Americans, though, didn't like the change. So, in 1941, Congress declared that Thanksgiving Day would officially fall on the fourth Thursday of November. And so it has ever since.

1. The author wrote the article mainly to
   Ⓐ explain the facts about Thanksgiving.
   Ⓑ describe the first Thanksgiving meal.
   Ⓒ convince readers not to eat turkey on Thanksgiving.
   Ⓓ entertain readers with an amusing story about Thanksgiving mistakes.

2. You know your answer to question 1 is correct because the article mainly
   Ⓐ contains many details that describe something.
   Ⓑ provides facts or tells readers how to do something.
   Ⓒ tries to convince readers of something.
   Ⓓ tells an enjoyable story.

Work with a partner. Talk about your answers to questions 1 and 2. Tell why you chose the answers you did.

Remember: Authors write to describe, to entertain, to explain, or to persuade.

★ As you read, ask yourself, "Does the reading passage contain many details that describe a person, place, or thing?" If so, the author's purpose is to describe.

★ As you read, ask yourself, "Does the reading passage tell an enjoyable or a personal story? Does the author use a story to teach a lesson?" If so, the author's purpose is to entertain.

★ As you read, ask yourself, "Does the reading passage provide facts about a particular subject? Does the passage tell me how to do something?" If so, the author's purpose is to explain.

★ As you read, ask yourself, "Does the reading passage try to convince me to do something, buy something, or believe something?" If so, the author's purpose is to persuade.

Read these instructions for an art project. As you read, ask yourself, "Why did the author probably write these instructions?" Then answer the questions.

Pendulum Art

If you suspend an object and give it a push, it will move back and forth at a regular rate. In science, this action is called *simple harmonic motion*. You can use this action to create some original art. The materials you will need are a bowl, a sheet of construction paper, a pencil, scissors, tape, a small plastic funnel, strong string, a large sheet of black paper, and a cup of salt.

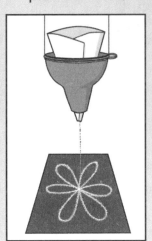

1. Trace the rim of the bowl on the construction paper and cut out the circle. Next, cut away a quarter of the circle. Then pull the sides of the circle together until they form a cone. Tape the cone together, but leave a small hole at the tip. Place the cone into the funnel.
2. Tie some string around the lip of the funnel. Use more string to suspend the funnel a few inches above a table or a counter surface.
3. Place the black paper under the funnel.
4. Block the funnel's tip with a finger, and pour in the salt.
5. Remove your finger, and push the funnel gently to make it swing. The salt will form a pattern on the black paper.

3. The author wrote the instructions mainly to
   Ⓐ persuade readers to study simple harmonic motion.
   Ⓑ describe what a pendulum is.
   Ⓒ explain how to do an art project.
   Ⓓ entertain readers with a story about a pendulum.

4. You know your answer to question 3 is correct because the instructions mainly
   Ⓐ contain many details that describe something.
   Ⓑ provide facts or tell readers how to do something.
   try to convince readers of something.
   Ⓓ tell an enjoyable story.

Look at the answer choices for each question. Read why each answer choice is correct or not correct.

3. The author wrote the instructions mainly to
   Ⓐ persuade readers to study simple harmonic motion.

   This answer is not correct because the instructions do not contain many convincing reasons that readers should study simple harmonic motion.

   Ⓑ describe what a pendulum is.

   This answer is not correct because the instructions do not contain many details that describe a pendulum.

   ● explain how to do an art project.

   This answer is correct because the instructions provide information that tells readers how to make pendulum art.

   Ⓓ entertain readers with a story about a pendulum.

   This answer is not correct because the instructions do not tell an interesting story or try to make readers laugh.

4. You know your answer to question 3 is correct because the instructions mainly
   Ⓐ contain many details that describe something.

   This answer is not correct because the instructions do not contain many details that describe a particular person, place, or thing.

   ● provide facts or tell readers how to do something.

   This answer is correct because the instructions do provide information that explains how to create pendulum art.

   Ⓒ try to convince readers of something.

   This answer is not correct because the instructions do not try to convince readers to do something, buy something, or believe something.

   Ⓓ tell an enjoyable story.

   This answer is not correct because the instructions do not tell an interesting story.

★ Each paragraph in a reading selection can have its own purpose. As you read each paragraph, ask yourself, "Why was this particular paragraph written? Is the author's purpose to describe, to entertain, to explain, or to persuade?"

★ The entire reading passage has one main purpose. After you have finished reading the passage, ask yourself, "Why was this passage mainly written? What did the author probably want readers to know?"

Read this article. Then answer the questions.

You've probably been warned many times to say no to drugs. You've probably also heard that not all drugs are bad. Doctors prescribe many drugs regularly. Good drugs relieve pain and cure and prevent illnesses. What you need to be concerned about are harmful drugs—the kind that can cause damage to the body and the mind.

All drugs sold on the street are dangerous and illegal. These drugs may contain harmful substances that can lead to health problems—and even death. Some legal drugs can be dangerous, too, if misused. Cigarettes, which contain the drug nicotine, are legal. So is alcohol. A problem occurs when a user likes the effects of the drug and needs to have some every day.

Young people often use drugs for all the wrong reasons. Here are some of the typical excuses:

- to relax
- to escape from problems
- to rebel against adults
- to impress other people
- to look older or to fit in
- to feel more awake or energetic
- to satisfy curiosity
- to improve sports ability

In the end, taking drugs is never satisfying. So, don't let others pressure you into experimenting with drugs. Resist! Dare to say no!

5. The author's main purpose in the first paragraph is to
   Ⓐ describe harmful drugs.
   Ⓑ explain the difference between good drugs and bad drugs.
   Ⓒ entertain readers with a personal story.
   Ⓓ persuade readers not to take drugs.

6. The author's main purpose in paragraph two is to
   Ⓐ describe dangerous drugs.
   Ⓑ explain why some drugs are legal.
   Ⓒ entertain readers with a riddle.
   Ⓓ persuade readers to avoid alcohol.

7. The author's main purpose in paragraph three is to
   Ⓐ describe a typical drug user.
   Ⓑ explain why youths use drugs.
   Ⓒ entertain readers with silly excuses.
   Ⓓ persuade readers to stay away from people who use drugs.

8. The article was written mainly to
   Ⓐ describe what a drug problem is.
   Ⓑ explain how drug problems begin.
   Ⓒ entertain readers with a fun story.
   Ⓓ persuade readers to resist harmful drugs.

Read this passage about the unicorn. Then answer the questions.

The hunter stood beside me
Who blew that mighty horn;
I saw that he was hunting
The gentle unicorn—
But the unicorn is noble,
He knows his gentle birth,
He knows that God has chosen him
Above all beasts of earth.

This German folk song honors a legendary creature. People from all parts of the world have told and written about the unicorn for thousands of years. The first description appeared about 400 B.C. Ctesias, a Greek physician had traveled to ancient Persia, where he heard many marvelous tales. Ctesias wrote that in India, there were wild donkeys that had a white body, dark-red head, and a pointed horn on the forehead. The horn was about 20 inches long and was white at the base, black in the middle, and bright red at the tip.

Over time, the image of the unicorn slowly changed. Eventually, the unicorn came to be a pure-white creature with the body and head of a small horse, the legs of a deer, the tail of a lion, and a magnificent twisted horn.

During the Middle Ages, people believed that the unicorn's horn had magical powers. It could provide protection against poisoning, illnesses, and evil. People paid a lot of money for the valuable horns. Most of these horns, though, were probably the tusks of narwhals. The narwhal is a small Arctic whale that has a spiral tusk growing from its snout.

Today, common belief is that there are no more unicorns on earth. Some people claim that unicorns were hunted until there were none left. Other people insist that unicorns never existed. Real or not, the legend of the extraordinary unicorn lives on.

9. The author wrote the first paragraph mainly to
   Ⓐ explain why unicorns have horns.
   Ⓑ persuade readers to visit Persia.
   Ⓒ describe what the first unicorns looked like.
   Ⓓ entertain readers with a fanciful legend.

10. The author wrote paragraph three mainly to
   Ⓐ persuade readers to learn more about the Middle Ages.
   Ⓑ explain that unicorn horns were probably narwhal tusks.
   Ⓒ describe what a narwhal looks like.
   Ⓓ entertain readers with a silly comparison.

11. The author wrote paragraph four mainly to
   Ⓐ explain why unicorns disappeared.
   Ⓑ convince readers that the unicorn—real or not—is special.
   Ⓒ amuse readers with a riddle.
   Ⓓ describe an imaginary creature.

12. The passage was written mainly to
   Ⓐ describe a noble creature.
   Ⓑ explain why the unicorn is legendary.
   Ⓒ entertain readers with a story about a magnificent beast.
   Ⓓ persuade readers that the unicorn had magical powers.

★ A test question about identifying the author's purpose may ask you why an author probably wrote a particular reading passage. This kind of question is asking about the purpose of the entire reading passage.

★ A test question about identifying the author's purpose may ask why a particular paragraph was written. This kind of question is asking about only one part of the reading passage.

★ A test question about identifying the author's purpose may ask what you think the author wants readers to know. To help you answer this type of test question, think about why the author probably wrote the reading passage.

Here is a clever poem. Read the poem. Then do Numbers 13 and 14.

Stately Verse

If Mary goes far out to sea,
  By wayward breezes fanned,
I'd like to know—can you tell me?—
  Just where would Maryland?

If Tenny went high up in the air
  And looked o'er land and lea,
Looked here and there and everywhere,
  Pray what would Tennessee?

I looked out of the window and
  Saw Orry on the lawn;
He's not there now, and who can tell
  Just where has Oregon?

Two girls were quarreling one day
  With garden tools, and so
I said, "My dears, let Mary rake
  And just let Idaho."

A friend of mine lived in a flat
  With half a dozen boys;
When he fell ill I asked him why.
  He said: "I'm Illinois."

An English lady had a steed.
  She called him Ighland Bay.
She rode for exercise, and thus
  Rhode Island every day.

Anonymous

Identifying Author's Purpose

13. The author wrote the poem mainly to
  Ⓐ explain how some states got their names.
  Ⓑ describe some girls and boys.
  Ⓒ convince readers to learn the names of all the states.
  Ⓓ entertain readers with a humorous play on words.

Identifying Author's Purpose

14. The author probably wants readers to know that
  Ⓐ silly stories can be made out of the names of some states.
  Ⓑ some states are named after people.
  Ⓒ they can write their own silly verses using state names.
  Ⓓ most state names have unusual origins.

Here is an invitation sent to students in Bell County. Read the invitation.
Then do Numbers 15 and 16.

Are you someone with big ideas?
Do you want to be known as someone who shaped the future?
If so, then here's an opportunity that might interest you.

WHAT: The Spirit of Invention Science Fair
WHO: Any student in grades 5 through 12 from the Bell County schools
WHEN: Saturday, April 7
  • Set up: 9:00 A.M.
  • Judging: 11:00 A.M.
  • Public viewing: 1:00–3:00 P.M.
WHERE: The George Washington Carver Auditorium, St. Louis, Missouri
HOW: 1. Research the invention you have in mind.
     (Remember: Simple inventions can also be a success!)
  2. Design a model of the invention.
  3. Create posters and write a journal describing the invention.
  4. Be prepared to explain to judges why your invention
     is important to society.
WHY: Top inventions at each grade level win a cash prize. The grand-prize winner wins the services of a patent attorney in the hopes of someday selling the invention in the marketplace.

Identifying Author's Purpose

15. The author uses an invitation format mainly to
    Ⓐ persuade students to design only simple inventions.
    Ⓑ describe what a successful invention is.
    Ⓒ explain all the facts students need to know about a science fair.
    Ⓓ entertain readers with a tale about a great inventor.

Identifying Author's Purpose

16. What is the main purpose of the "why" part of the invitation?
    Ⓐ to convince students to enter a science fair
    Ⓑ to describe what a patent attorney does
    Ⓒ to explain that everyone wins a prize
    Ⓓ to delight readers with information about prizes

PART ONE: LEARN ABOUT INTERPRETING FIGURATIVE LANGUAGE

Read this sentence. As you read, think about the two things being compared.

> **The hour passed slowly, like a turtle crawling in sand.**
> The two things being compared are an hour and a turtle.
> The writer used a **simile** to help readers picture how slowly the hour passed.
> A simile uses the word *like* or *as* to compare two things.

Read this sentence. As you read, think about the two things being compared.

> **The stars are brilliant diamonds in a black sky.**
> The two things being compared are stars and diamonds.
> The writer used a **metaphor** to help readers picture the sight of the stars.
> A metaphor compares two things but does not use the word *like* or *as*.
> A metaphor says that one thing *is* another thing.

Now read this sentence. As you read, think about the meaning of the underlined words.

> **Manuel and Michael met at camp and really <u>hit it off</u>.**
> The underlined words mean that the boys quickly became good friends.
> The underlined words are an **idiom**.
> An idiom is a phrase whose words have a meaning different from their usual meaning.

Similes, metaphors, and idioms are types of figurative language. Authors use figurative language to help readers create pictures in their mind. When you understand the meaning of a simile, a metaphor, or an idiom, you are **interpreting figurative language**.

★ Look for things that are compared in a reading passage. Try to find examples of similes or metaphors.

★ Look for phrases whose words have a meaning different from their usual meaning. Try to find examples of idioms.

★ Figurative language usually brings a picture to a reader's mind. Use that picture to help you understand the meaning of the figurative language.

Read this description of a tall-tale hero. As you read, ask yourself, "What pictures come to mind?" Then answer the questions.

Big Mose

Big Mose was once the bravest fireman in New York City. He was also the biggest and the strongest. He could carry streetcars and swim all the way around Manhattan Island in just six strokes. Mose stood eight feet tall and wore a stovepipe hat that made him two feet taller. His hands were as large as Virginia hams. He had flaming red hair and eyes that twinkled with mischief. His laughter sounded like the roar of Niagara Falls and caused buildings to shake.

In Mose's day, fire engines looked like big wagons with long handles on the sides. They had a condenser in the middle and a long hose. Firemen would pump water through the condenser into the hose and toward the flames. The old fire machines had no engines or horses to move them along. It took dozens of firemen to pull each machine through the city streets.

Mose's fire machine was called *Lady Washington*. She was the finest fire machine in the city. Mose loved that "old gal." It made his heart proud to run alongside her.

Mose had a heart of gold and always did his duty. When a fire alarm sounded, he was the first one to arrive at the firehouse and pull on his striped suspenders, bright-red shirt, and giant boots and fire helmet. He walked through flames as if they were made of bricks. All kinds of people thanked him for saving their life. "Just doing my duty," he would always reply.

1. In the first paragraph, Mose's laughter is compared to
   Ⓐ a ringing fire alarm.
   Ⓑ an old fire machine.
   Ⓒ the sound of falling bricks.
   Ⓓ the roar of Niagara Falls.

2. In the last paragraph, the phrase *had a heart of gold* means that Mose was
   Ⓐ interested in being rich.
   Ⓑ generous and friendly.
   Ⓒ selfish and unkind.
   Ⓓ wealthy in many ways.

 Work with a partner. Talk about your answers to questions 1 and 2. Tell why you chose the answers you did.

Remember: Similes, metaphors, and idioms are types of figurative language. Authors use figurative language to help readers create clear pictures in their mind.

★ Look for things that are compared in a reading passage. See if the word *like* or *as* is used, or if a sentence says that one thing is another thing.

★ Look for phrases whose words have a meaning different from their usual meaning.

★ Think about any pictures that come to mind as you read. Use those pictures to help you understand what is being described.

Read this fable from Aesop. As you read, look for things that are compared. Also look for words that have a meaning different from their usual meaning. Then answer the questions.

The Miser

A miser sold everything he had for a bag of gold coins. He melted down the gold into a single lump, which he buried secretly in a field. Every day, he went to look at the spot. Sometimes, he would spend long hours gloating over his treasure. A man noticed the miser's frequent visits to the field and one day watched him and discovered his secret. One night, the man waited for just the right moment, and then he dug up the gold and carried it away.

The next day, the miser visited the place as usual. Finding his treasure gone, his face darkened like a cloud. Then he began tearing out his hair and groaning over his loss. One of his neighbors saw him in this condition and asked the miser what his trouble was. The miser told the man of his misfortune. "Don't take it so much to heart, my friend," the man replied. "Put a brick into the hole and take a look at it every day. You won't be any worse off than before, for even when you had your gold, it was of no use to you."

3. In paragraph two, the miser's face is compared to
   Ⓐ a lump of gold.
   Ⓑ a brick.
   Ⓒ a cloud.
   Ⓓ a storm.

4. In paragraph two, the phrase *take it to heart* means
   Ⓐ "hold something against the heart."
   Ⓑ "take something seriously."
   Ⓒ "act stingy with money."
   Ⓓ "enjoy something too much."

Look at the answer choices for each question. Read why each answer choice is correct or not correct.

3. In paragraph two, the miser's face is compared to

   Ⓐ a lump of gold.

   This answer is not correct because there is no comparison between the miser's face and a lump of gold.

   Ⓑ a brick.

   This answer is not correct because there is no comparison between the miser's face and a brick.

   ● a cloud.

   This answer is correct because the paragraph actually states that the miser's face darkened like a cloud. The word like *signals that two things are being compared in a simile.*

   Ⓓ a storm.

   This answer is not correct because the word storm *is not used in the fable.*

4. In paragraph two, the phrase *take it to heart* means

   Ⓐ "hold something against the heart."

   This answer is not correct because there are no details in the fable to hint at this meaning of the phrase. The miser's treasure is gone; it would be impossible for him to hold it against his heart.

   ● "take something seriously."

   This answer is correct because the details in the fable suggest that the miser was taking the loss of his treasure very seriously. His face darkened like a cloud, he tore out his hair, and he groaned.

   Ⓒ "act stingy with money."

   This answer is not correct because there are no details in the paragraph to hint at this meaning. The miser cannot be stingy with something he no longer has.

   Ⓓ "enjoy something too much."

   This answer is not correct because there are no details in the fable to hint at this meaning. The miser is upset that he lost his gold; therefore, he could not be enjoying anything at the moment.

★ Think about the things being compared in a simile or metaphor. Ask yourself, "What do the two things have in common?" This will help you create pictures in your mind.

★ Look at the sentences near an idiom. You might find context clues to help you figure out its meaning.

Read this radio interview. Then answer the questions.

Interviewer: We'd like to welcome the director Dred Fuller to our show. Mr. Fuller is the Steven Spielberg of horror films. Tell us, Dred, how did you become so interested in monsters?

Dred Fuller: Everyone is fascinated by monsters, not just me. For some strange reason, we enjoy things that scare the daylights out of us.

Interviewer: Let's talk about your latest film, *The Werewolf of Los Angeles*. Where did you get the idea for this movie?

Dred Fuller: When I was a kid, I saw the classic film *The Wolf Man*. This movie blew my mind. The story is about a young man who gets bitten by a werewolf. Afterwards, whenever there was a full moon, the man would turn into a werewolf and kill innocent people. The werewolf was a hairy two-legged creature with fangs as sharp as daggers. Each time it appeared on screen, I screamed as loud as the beast.

Interviewer: What is your next project?

Dred Fuller: I'm making a new movie version of the novel *Frankenstein*, by Mary Shelley. My film will be called *Frankly Frankenstein*.

5. The interviewer compares Dred Fuller to
   Ⓐ the Wolf Man.
   Ⓑ Frankenstein.
   Ⓒ Steven Spielberg.
   Ⓓ Mary Shelley.

6. The phrase *scare the daylights out of* means
   Ⓐ "make someone afraid of the dark."
   Ⓑ "frighten someone a lot."
   Ⓒ "shut off the lights."
   Ⓓ "turn day into night."

7. What does the phrase *blew my mind* mean?
   Ⓐ "caused excitement"
   Ⓑ "prevented something"
   Ⓒ "caused hatred"
   Ⓓ "have a headache"

8. The sharpness of the werewolf's fangs is compared to that of
   Ⓐ knives.
   Ⓑ razors.
   Ⓒ needles.
   Ⓓ daggers.

Read this amusing poem. Then answer the questions.

Uncle Setchell
by stevan-adele Morley and Robert G. Forest

Uncle Setchell has hair that sticks out like thatch,
White as raw turnip from a vegetable patch.
He combs it in haste, using fingers for tines,
And pulls at the snarls entangled like vines.
He's a grizzly brown bear with leatherhide skin
And porcupine whiskers that blanket his chin.
A man of good humor, blue eyes all aglow,
He greets each new day with a thunderous "Hello."
His hands are like vises; they're tight in the clutch.
He doesn't speak often and never says much.
He chews on a matchstick at the side of his mouth
And fishes for hours in the crick to the south.
He favor's ol' Gator—he's fond of the hound
That sticks to his side like an oak sticks to ground.
Each Saturday, Aunt Nettie sets out the wood tub
And pleads with her husband to bathe and to scrub.
He scowls and he scoffs and scolds with disgust,
"Let me outta this tub; I'm beginning to rust!"

9. In the first line, Uncle Setchell's hair is compared to
Ⓐ sticks.
Ⓑ porcupine whiskers.
Ⓒ thatch.
Ⓓ a vegetable patch.

10. Which two things are compared in the poem?
Ⓐ brown hair and raw turnips
Ⓑ snarled hair and tangled vines
Ⓒ skin and a blanket
Ⓓ blue eyes and the sky

11. The words *His hands are like vises* mean that Uncle Setchell's hands
Ⓐ have a strong grip.
Ⓑ are always closed in a tight fist.
Ⓒ look like clamping devices.
Ⓓ snap shut with great force.

12. Which of these is a metaphor?
Ⓐ He's a man of good humor.
Ⓑ His hound sticks to his side like an oak sticks to ground.
Ⓒ He scowls and he scoffs and scolds with disgust.
Ⓓ He's a grizzly brown bear.

★ A test question about interpreting figurative language may ask you about the meaning of a particular simile, metaphor, or idiom.

★ A test question about interpreting figurative language, may ask you to identify a particular type of figurative language, such as a simile, a metaphor, or an idiom.

Here is an article about a natural wonder. Read the article. Then do Numbers 13 and 14.

An Unnatural Natural Wonder

In central Australia, a huge rock rises out of the flat desert. The Aborigines call the rock Uluru. The name means "great pebble." From a distance, the rock looks like a giant pebble sitting on a level plain. Uluru, which is also called Ayers Rock, is visible from more than 50 miles away. It is the largest single rock in the world. The rock is about 1.5 miles long and a mile wide. It stands about as tall as the Empire State Building, in New York. The rock rises 1,143 feet high above the desert floor. However, there may be twice as much rock below the ground as above it.

Uluru is made of red sandstone. The rock was formed under the sea about 600 million years ago. Earth movements pushed it above sea level and tilted it. The rock changes color as the sun moves across the sky. At dawn, Uluru is a bright red ball of fire. Later in the day, it turns a deep orange yellow. Sometimes, it is violet.

Aborigines know Uluru as "the place where the wind moans between sunset and dawn." The desert winds blow strongly at the top of the rock. Scientists believe that wind erosion continues to change the rock's surface. The Aborigines, though, believe that Uluru does not change. They and their ancestors have lived around Uluru for 10,000 years and see it as a sacred place. The Aborigines believe that their ancestors made the rock and the land around it. These ancestors lived long, long ago during a time called tjukurpa, or the Dream Time. The ancestors had great adventures that, once and for all, changed the flat earth. A valley near Uluru is the path one ancestor walked during tjukurpa. Scratches in Uluru are spear marks from a great battle. A hole shows where an ancestor sat to rest. A nearby mountain is an ancestor who has fallen asleep.

Interpreting Figurative Language

13. In the first paragraph, Uluru's size is compared to
    Ⓐ a level plain.
    Ⓑ the Empire State Building.
    Ⓒ a bright red ball of fire.
    Ⓓ the setting sun.

Interpreting Figurative Language

14. Which of these is a simile?
    Ⓐ At dawn, Uluru is a bright red ball of fire.
    Ⓑ Uluru stands as tall as the Empire State Building.
    Ⓒ Uluru is the place where the wind moans.
    Ⓓ A nearby mountain is an ancestor who has fallen asleep.

Here is a Norse myth. Read the myth. Then do Numbers 15 and 16.

How Thor Lost His Hammer

Many of our days of the week are named after Norse gods and goddesses. For example, Thursday is named for Thor, the god of thunder.

Thor was the oldest son of Odin, king of all the gods. Thor was a large and powerful man. His temper was as mighty as his strength. Sometimes, his fury was so wild that sparks flew from his red beard and his eyes burned as red as embers. Thor rode in a chariot drawn by two goats, and he carried a magic hammer called Mjolnir, or Thunderbolt. Whenever Thor swung his hammer, lightning flashed in the sky. Thor used Mjolnir to protect the gods against the forces of evil. The hammer crushed whatever it hit. It never missed its target and always flew back to Thor's hand.

One night while Thor slept, Thrym, who was king of all the giants, stole Thor's hammer. Thrym then buried the hammer eight miles underground. He refused to give it back unless Freya, the goddess of beauty, became his wife.

Freya threw a fit when she heard about Thrym's command. She refused to have a hideous giant for a husband. At last, it was decided that Thor must disguise himself as a bride and go to Thrym. Loki, the mischief maker, would dress as a maid and accompany him.

When the two arrived in the world of the giants, they saw that Thrym had prepared a wedding feast. As soon as everyone was seated at the table, "Freya" began devouring great quantities of food.

"Never have I seen a bride eat more!" Thrym exclaimed.

"She hasn't eaten for eight days," Loki explained. "She has been too excited about meeting you."

Thrym then lifted up his bride's veil to kiss her. But when his eyes met hers, he screamed. "Why do Freya's eyes burn like fire?" he cried.

"Her eyes burn because she has not slept for eight nights," said Loki.

"Very well then," said Thrym. "Bring forth Thor's hammer, and let us make our marriage vows."

As soon as the hammer was placed in the bride's lap, Thor stood up and began swinging. The hammer killed Thrym and then one giant after another. Afterward, Thor and Loki jumped into the chariot and carried Thor's hammer back to the land of the gods.

Interpreting Figurative Language

15. In paragraph two, Thor's eyes are compared to
    Ⓐ lightning.
    Ⓑ sparks.
    Ⓒ red embers.
    Ⓓ the sky.

Interpreting Figurative Language

16. In paragraph four, the phrase *threw a fit* means
    Ⓐ "got confused."
    Ⓑ "behaved carelessly."
    Ⓒ "tossed things into the air."
    Ⓓ "became angry."

PART ONE: LEARN ABOUT SUMMARIZING

Read this article about Thomas Jefferson. As you read, think about the most important ideas in the article. Then think about what you might tell someone who asks what the article is about.

Thomas Jefferson was the third president of the United States. He wrote the Declaration of Independence and was a great man with many ideas and interests. He was an architect, an inventor, and a musician. Some people believe that he had a brilliant mind. While entertaining a group of Nobel Prize winners, president John F. Kennedy once remarked, "I think this is the most extraordinary collection of talent and human knowledge that has ever been gathered at the White House, with the possible exception of when Thomas Jefferson dined alone."

The most important ideas in the article are

Thomas Jefferson was the third president of the United States.

He was a great man with many ideas and interests.

Some people believe that he had a brilliant mind.

What you might tell someone who asks what the article is about.

Thomas Jefferson, the third president of the United States, was a brilliant man with many ideas and a variety of interests.

The statement above is a summary. A summary is a short statement that tells the main points or important ideas of a reading passage. When you restate the important ideas in a short statement, you are **summarizing**.

★ A summary is not stated in a reading passage. To create a summary, you must think about and restate the most important ideas.

★ A good summary of fiction tells about the main character's problem and its solution.

★ A good summary of nonfiction tells about the main idea of the reading selection, as well as the main idea of each paragraph.

Read this famous American short story. As you read, think about the main character's problem and its solution. Then answer the questions.

In a village at the foot of the Catskill Mountains, there once lived a cheerful but lazy farmer named Rip Van Winkle. He was married to a woman who was always demanding that he do his chores. One day, Rip got tired of being pestered. So he took his dog and gun and climbed up the mountains to hunt.

On the mountainside, Rip met an odd little man who was trying to carry a barrel up the mountain. Rip helped the man bring the barrel to a cave, where he met more little men. The odd hosts kindly offered their guest a drink from the barrel. After two swallows, Rip fell into a deep sleep.

When he awoke, there was no sign of the little men. Rip reached for his shiny gun, but a rusted gun lay in its spot instead. He called his dog, but it never appeared. He was also surprised to find that his joints felt stiff, his clothes were ragged, and he had a long gray beard.

Rip returned to his village and saw that it was greatly changed. When he went to his home, he discovered that strangers were living there. He learned that his wife had died, his children had grown, and that he, in fact, had been asleep for twenty years.

In time, Rip got used to his new surroundings and enjoyed being the oldest person in the village. Each evening, he sat down at the local inn and told stories. The one he told most, of course, was the one about himself.

1. What is Rip Van Winkle's problem in the story?
   Ⓐ He cannot change his lazy ways.
   Ⓑ While hiding from his wife, his life changes greatly.
   Ⓒ He loses his dog while hunting in the mountains.
   Ⓓ He is tricked by a group of wicked little men.

2. What is the best summary of the story?
   Ⓐ A farmer grows old instantly.
   Ⓑ A farmer tries to help a little man but is tricked instead.
   Ⓒ A farmer returns from a hunting trip to find that his world has changed.
   Ⓓ A farmer learns that he likes to tell stories.

Work with a partner. Talk about your answers to questions 1 and 2. Tell why you chose the answers you did.

Remember: A summary is a short statement that tells the main points or important ideas of a reading passage.

★ A good summary of fiction tells about the main character's problem and its solution.

★ A good summary of nonfiction includes the main ideas of the selection.

Read this article about measurements. As you read, ask yourself, "What does a good summary of nonfiction include?" Then answer the questions.

When a Foot Is Not a Foot

INCH?

Today, in the United States, standards for measures—such as inches, feet, and yards—are kept by the National Institute of Standards and Technology. But the standards for early measures varied.

Some early measures were based on the size of body parts. For example, the first inch was the width of a person's thumb. In fact, the English word *inch* probably comes from the Latin word *unica*, which means "thumb." In 1324, King Edward II of England gave this measure a "thumbs down." Thumb widths can vary, and the king wanted a more exact standard that could be used by everyone. So, he chose barleycorns as the official measure for inches. By the king's rule, "three grains of barley—placed end to end" equaled an inch.

In ancient times, the foot was the length of an average man's foot. But human feet come in many sizes. Therefore, King Edward II said that a foot should be equal to 36 barley corns set end to end. This measure was approximately 12 inches.

The yard was probably first used by merchants to measure cloth. The end of the cloth was held in one outstretched arm while the other arm brought a length of cloth to the nose. You could buy a longer yard from a merchant with a long arm than from a merchant with a short arm.

3. What is the main idea of the article?
   Ⓐ A national institute keeps standards for measures.
   Ⓑ King Edward II created standards for measures.
   Ⓒ Some early measures were based on thumb width and foot length.
   Ⓓ The standards for early measures varied.

4. What is a good summary of the article?
   Ⓐ King Edward II was the first person to demand more exact standards for measures.
   Ⓑ Standards for measures have always varied.
   Ⓒ The standards for measures have become more exact over time.
   Ⓓ Barleycorns were once a standard measure for inches and feet.

SUMMARIZING

Look at the answer choices for each question. Read why each answer choice is correct or not correct.

3. What is the main idea of the article?

Ⓐ A national institute keeps standards for measures.

   This answer is not correct because it does not tell what the article is mostly about. The answer tells only a detail that supports the main idea.

Ⓑ King Edward II created standards for measures.

   This answer is not correct because it does not tell what the article is mostly about. The answer tells only a detail that supports the main idea.

Ⓒ Some early measures were based on thumb width and foot length.

   This answer is not correct because it does not tell what the article is mostly about. The answer tells only details that support the main idea.

● The standards for early measures varied.

   This answer is correct because it tells what the article is mostly about. The main idea is stated in the last sentence of the first paragraph. The other facts and details in the article support this main idea.

4. What is a good summary of the article?

Ⓐ King Edward II was the first person to demand more exact standards for measures.

   This answer is not correct because it does not contain the most important ideas in the article, as a good summary of nonfiction should.

Ⓑ Standards for measures have always varied.

   This answer is not correct because this information is inaccurate. According to the article, standards for measures once varied but are now kept the same by the National Institute of Standards and Technology.

● The standards for measures have become more exact over time.

   This answer is correct because it includes the most important ideas in the article.

Ⓓ Barleycorns were once a standard measure for inches and feet.

   This answer is not correct because it states only one important detail from the article. A good summary of nonfiction includes the main ideas of the selection.

★ A good summary of fiction often includes a statement of the theme.

★ A good summary of nonfiction answers *who, what, when, where, why,* and *how* questions.

Read this article about different kinds of vehicles. Then answer the questions.

People today may think that city streets are too crowded with traffic. Yet, city streets have always been filled with traffic. Only the vehicles have changed!

In the 1800s, people got around American cities by taking the horsecar. It was a covered carriage pulled by horses. It ran along rails sunk into the street. The larger horsecars could seat more than a dozen people.

In the 1880s, cities began adopting a new kind of "streetcar." Instead of being pulled by horses, it was pulled along by cables overhead. The cables were powered by electricity. City streets soon filled with the screeching of metal wheels against metal tracks, and the clanging of bells.

In the early 1900s, a strange vehicle appeared. It had an engine and ran without being connected to wires. People called it a horseless carriage. Before long, these vehicles were everywhere. They were, of course, the first automobiles. Built-up automobiles, called motorbuses, shortly replaced any horsecars still traveling city streets. By the 1930s, "buses" had replaced almost all the electric streetcars.

5. What is the article mostly about?
   Ⓐ using buses for city travel
   Ⓑ traffic crowds in cities
   Ⓒ the disappearance of horsecars
   Ⓓ vehicles that have traveled city streets

6. Which of these were rarely seen on city streets after 1930?
   Ⓐ horseless carriages
   Ⓑ electric streetcars
   Ⓒ buses
   Ⓓ automobiles

7. Why was the automobile important to city travel?
   Ⓐ It was safer than riding a horse.
   Ⓑ It could carry more people.
   Ⓒ It had an engine, so it didn't have to be pulled.
   Ⓓ It was less noisy.

8. What is a good summary of the article?
   Ⓐ Automobiles and buses replaced horsecars and streetcars during the early 1900s.
   Ⓑ Traffic once crowded city streets.
   Ⓒ Horsecars and streetcars were the first forms of transportation.
   Ⓓ City streets have always been filled with vehicles.

SUMMARIZING

Read this Aztec legend. Then answer the questions.

The Hummingbird Guide

Long ago, the Aztec lived in the dry desert with the cactus. Life was hard. So their god Huitzilopochtli, the hummingbird god, told the Aztec to seek a new home. He also gave the people a new name: Mexica.

The Mexica found a beautiful land of clear sun and bright blue skies. They settled in Aztlan, the "place of the herons." Life seemed good. But all too soon, Huitzilopochtli told the priests that Aztlan was not to be their home. So the priests, carrying statues of Huitzilopochtli on their backs, and the Mexica set out to look for their new home. They wandered year after year. Each time they found a place to settle, they built a temple to their god. But each time, Huitzilopochtli told them to move again. He promised the priests a sign to mark the new home.

The Mexica wandered into the Valley of Mexico. The rich land was crowded with many peoples, and none wanted the Mexica to live there. Finally, an angry group chased them into Lake Texcoco. The Mexica took refuge on an island in the lake. Huitzilopochtli appeared to the priests and ordered them to look among the reeds for the sign: an eagle with a snake in its mouth standing on a cactus! The grateful Mexica built their city on the island, with a great temple for their god. The city was Tenochtitlán, or "place of the prickly-pear cactus fruit."

9. Who are the main characters in the legend?
   Ⓐ the Aztec and the Mexica
   Ⓑ the hummingbird god and the Mexica
   Ⓒ the eagle and the Mexica
   Ⓓ the priests and the Mexica

10. What did the Mexica's god do?
   Ⓐ He ordered the Mexica to build temples to him.
   Ⓑ He created a great city.
   Ⓒ He told the Mexica to move again and again.
   Ⓓ He forced the Mexica to leave the Valley of Mexico.

11. What did the Mexica do?
   Ⓐ They built a temple to their god in each place they settled.
   Ⓑ They looked for a home where life would be easier.
   Ⓒ They built a city in Aztlan.
   Ⓓ They built temples to their gods throughout Mexico.

12. What is a good summary of the legend?
   Ⓐ The Mexica moved many times until they received a sign that they should make their home in Tenochtitlán.
   Ⓑ The hummingbird god ordered the Mexica to build him a great temple in their final homeland.
   Ⓒ The Mexica settled in Aztlan, where they built a temple to their god.
   Ⓓ The hummingbird god ordered the Mexica to move to an island in Lake Texcoco.

★ A test question about summarizing may ask you to choose the best summary of a reading passage. When you answer questions about summarizing, first determine if the reading passage is a work of fiction or nonfiction. Then think about what is included in a good summary of fiction and a good summary of nonfiction.

★ The answer to a test question about summarizing will not be directly stated in the reading passage. You must think about the most important ideas to find the best summary.

Here is a song sung by Confederate soldiers during the Civil War. Read the song. Then answer the questions.

Sitting by the roadside on a summer day,
Chatting with my messmates, passing time away.
Lying in the shadow, underneath the trees,
Goodness how delicious, eating goober peas!

When a horseman passes, the soldiers have a rule:
To cry out at their loudest, "Mister, here's your mule!"
But another pleasure, enchantinger than these,
Is wearing out your grinders eating goober peas!

Just before the battle, the gen'ral hears a row.
He says, "The Yanks are coming; I hear their rifles now."
He turns around in wonder, and what do you think he sees?
The Georgia militia—eating goober peas!

I think my song has lasted almost long enough,
The subject's interesting, but rhymes are might rough.
I wish this war was over, when free from rags and fleas,
We'd kiss our wives and sweethearts, and gobble goober peas!

Summarizing

13. The song is mostly about
    Ⓐ eating too many goober peas.
    Ⓑ sitting by the roadside.
    Ⓒ dreaming of eating goober peas.
    Ⓓ looking for something to do between battles.

Summarizing

14. What is a good summary of the song?
    Ⓐ A soldier takes his mind off war by dreaming of eating goober peas.
    Ⓑ A soldier passes the time between battles by lying in the shade.
    Ⓒ A soldier thinks that goober peas are delicious.
    Ⓓ A soldier takes pleasure in chatting with his messmates.

Here is a short biography of a pioneer for women's rights. Read the biography. Then do Numbers 15 and 16.

In 1820, the year Susan B. Anthony was born, women had almost no rights. They could not speak in public, attend high school or college, or vote. They were also not allowed to own property, run a business, or hold public office.

Susan B. Anthony was born into a Quaker family. Like all Quakers, she grew up believing that men and women are equals. Later, Anthony realized that not everyone shared this belief. As a teacher, she earned three times less than the male teachers.

In 1851, Anthony met Elizabeth Cady Stanton, a leader in the women's rights movement. The two women worked together for more than 50 years. Their biggest goal was for women to be granted the right to vote.

On November 1, 1872, Anthony led 15 women into a voter-registration office in New York. They were asked to leave, but Anthony refused. Instead, she read aloud the Fourteenth and Fifteenth Amendments to the Constitution. They state that all people born in the United States are citizens, and that the right to vote shall not be denied to citizens. Four days later, the women broke the law and cast their vote for president of the United States.

Three weeks later, all 16 women were arrested. They had broken a federal law that stated that anyone who votes without having a legal right to do so is guilty of a crime. Only Anthony, however, stood trial. She was found guilty and fined $100. She never paid the fine.

Until her death, at age 86, Anthony devoted all of her time and energy to the women's movement. In the 1890s, four states—Wyoming, Colorado, Idaho, and Utah—finally gave women the right to vote. Then, in 1920 (14 years after Anthony died), the Nineteenth Amendment became law. At last, all women in the United States were granted the right to vote.

In 1979, the United States government issued a new one-dollar coin. This coin had Susan B. Anthony's picture on it. She was the first woman to be so honored.

Summarizing

15. Why was Susan B. Anthony an important person?
    - Ⓐ She was the first woman to have her image on a coin.
    - Ⓑ She was a great leader of the women's rights movement.
    - Ⓒ She stood trial for her belief in women's right to vote.
    - Ⓓ She worked closely with Elizabeth Cady Stanton.

Summarizing

16. Which of these is the best summary of the biography?
    - Ⓐ Susan B. Anthony devoted her life to the struggle for women's rights, especially their right to vote.
    - Ⓑ Susan B. Anthony worked with Elizabeth Cady Stanton for 50 years to get equal rights for women.
    - Ⓒ Susan B. Anthony was a Quaker who believed that men and women are equals.
    - Ⓓ Susan B. Anthony did not rest until all women were granted the right to vote.

PART ONE: READ A FABLE

Here is a fable from India. Read the fable. Then do Numbers 1 through 6.

The Wise Old Goose

A flock of wild geese lived safely and peacefully in the high branches of a tree in the forest. One day, the oldest goose looked down at the base of the tree and saw a vine beginning to creep its way up the trunk. "We must pull up that vine before it brings us harm," he told the others. "We cannot allow it to grow any higher."

"It is only a plant," said one of the younger geese. "It cannot hurt us."

"Let us destroy it now while it is weak and small," the old goose insisted. "It will be dangerous when it is big." The younger geese laughed and snickered at the foolishness of the old goose. He heard their comments and sighed sadly.

So the vine was allowed to creep up the tree. It grew thicker and stronger, winding itself round and round until it had reached the geese's home.

One morning, a trapper carrying a large net noticed the vine creeping up the tree trunk. It looked just like a ladder. The trapper lifted his eyes to the upper branches. When he saw the flock of geese, his heart leaped with hope.

Quietly, stealthily, the trapper climbed the vine. He spread out his net, and then he descended. By evening, every goose had stumbled or flown into the net.

"How did the trapper get up here?" they asked one another.

"It must have been that creeping vine!" replied one of them. Then they remembered the advice of the wise old goose. Oh, if only they had listened!

The younger geese now turned to the old one. He, too, had been caught in the net. "Please forgive us," the younger geese pleaded. "We're so sorry that we ever doubted your wisdom. Please, tell us how to get out of this trap!"

The old goose remained silent, but his thoughts began to whirl. A plan came to him. He explained it to the other geese, and this time, they paid close attention.

At dawn, the trapper climbed the tree, expecting to find geese struggling in his net. Instead, he found the birds lying stiffly, feet in the air. "They are all dead," he thought unhappily. "They must have been ill." Then he began plucking the geese out of the net one by one and tossing them to the ground. When the last goose was dropped, all of the birds flapped their wings and flew off, safe and sound.

The trapper gazed at the flock, astonished. "These are the smartest geese I have ever seen in my life!" he cried out. Then he gathered up his net, climbed down the vine, and walked off, still shaking his head in amazement.

Identifying Author's Purpose

1. What is the author's purpose
    in paragraph three?
    Ⓐ to show that the younger geese do
    not share the old goose's concerns
    Ⓑ to describe a creeping vine
    Ⓒ to convince readers that the old goose
    is foolish
    Ⓓ to make readers laugh at the younger
    geese's comments

Interpreting Figurative Language

4. In the next-to-last paragraph, the phrase
    safe and sound means
    Ⓐ "protected from illness."
    Ⓑ "free of all noise."
    Ⓒ "able to hear well."
    Ⓓ "unharmed in any way."

Identifying Author's Purpose

2. The fable was written mainly to
    Ⓐ describe the foolishness of geese.
    Ⓑ persuade readers to solve
    their own problems.
    Ⓒ inform readers about one way
    to escape from a trap.
    Ⓓ entertain readers with a story
    that teaches a lesson.

Summarizing

5. The fable is mostly about
    Ⓐ a flock of geese that narrowly escapes
    a trapper's net.
    Ⓑ smart geese that think up
    a clever escape plan.
    Ⓒ younger geese that learn from
    a wise old goose.
    Ⓓ a creeping vine that becomes
    a great danger.

Interpreting Figurative Language

3. In paragraph five, the writer compares
    the creeping vine to
    Ⓐ a corkscrew.
    Ⓑ a ladder.
    Ⓒ a trap.
    Ⓓ a thick, strong rope.

Summarizing

6. What is the best summary of the fable?
    Ⓐ A flock of geese refuses to see that
    a creeping vine is dangerous.
    Ⓑ A flock of geese ignores a wise old
    goose's advice but finally listens when
    its life is in danger.
    Ⓒ A flock of smart geese fools a trapper
    by pretending to be dead.
    Ⓓ A trapper climbs up a vine and traps
    some geese in his net, but they escape.

Here is a news story about an event that occurred in Maine. Read the news story. Then do Numbers 7 through 12.

Tuesday, March 9, 1999

Can Opener Lures Lost Cat Home

Oakland, Maine (AP) Precious the cat spent 19 days lost in a strange area. But now he is safe at home after hearing a tape recording of his favorite sound—the grinding of an electric can opener.

Precious' problems began on Christmas Eve. That night, Lincoln and Dawna DeMarey crashed their car into a guardrail on Interstate 95 in Waterville, 100 miles from home. The crash threw Precious' cat carrier from the car. When a rescuer picked up the carrier, the top came off, and the frightened cat dashed into the woods.

"We'd given up. I'd thrown away all of his records and everything," Lincoln DeMarey said.

But Waterville rescue workers Tony Brown and Janice Bradbury never gave up hope that they'd find the feline. Last Friday, someone spotted Precious.

"I couldn't believe my ears," Bradbury said. "Somebody had seen the cat."

Hugh Doucette, who lives about two miles from the crash site, had been feeding the cat.

"But I didn't put two and two together until the next morning that this was the missing cat I had read about in the newspaper," Doucette said.

Doucette alerted authorities. Bradbury arrived on the scene with a tape the desperate DeMareys had made of their voices calling Precious, and of the cat's beloved electric can opener.

Precious came within ten minutes. Neighbors snagged him when he made a run for the tape recorder.

DeMarey said his cat came home thin and exhausted, but happy to be home.

"Last night he hopped up on our bed right between us. He's curled up and sleeping now. He seems very happy," he said.

Identifying Author's Purpose

7. What is the author's purpose in paragraph two?
   - (A) to entertain readers with the tale of a strange cat
   - (B) to describe for readers what Precious looks like
   - (C) to persuade readers that they should drive carefully
   - (D) to explain to readers how Precious got lost

Interpreting Figurative Language

10. In paragraph seven, the phrase *put two and two together* means
    - (A) "connect two ideas with two more ideas."
    - (B) "add 2 and 2 to make 4."
    - (C) "figure something out from the information available."
    - (D) "know a lot about someone or something."

Identifying Author's Purpose

8. The news story was written mainly to
   - (A) amuse readers with a true story about an unusual cat.
   - (B) convince readers to take good care of their pets.
   - (C) explain a way to find a lost cat.
   - (D) describe a peculiar cat.

Summarizing

11. What is the main idea of the news story?
    - (A) Precious is a special cat.
    - (B) Rescue workers find a lost cat.
    - (C) A lost cat is drawn home by a favorite sound.
    - (D) In Maine, people care about cats.

Interpreting Figurative Language

9. Janice Bradbury said, *"I couldn't believe my ears."* This sentence means that she
   - (A) heard ringing in her ears.
   - (B) could not believe what she was hearing.
   - (C) could not believe what she was seeing.
   - (D) was sad to hear bad news.

Summarizing

12. Which of these best summarizes the news story?
    - (A) A lost cat arrives home safely after hearing a tape recording of an electric can opener.
    - (B) Rescue workers never give up hope of finding a lost cat.
    - (C) A lost cat comes home thin and exhausted, but safe.
    - (D) A Christmas Eve crash causes a Maine couple to lose their beloved cat.

PART ONE: READ A TALL TALE

Here is a tall tale about a cowboy hero. Read the tale.
Then do Numbers 1 through 12.

Pecos Bill was the greatest cowboy who ever lived. Before he came along, cowboys didn't know much about their job. They just rode around the cows, yelping and hollering. Pecos Bill taught the cowboys how to round up cattle and drive the herds. He also invented the six-shooter, the branding iron, and the lasso.

When Bill was a baby, his family lived in eastern Texas. One day, his father heard of another family moving in about 50 miles away. Having neighbors that close was too crowded for him. So, he and his wife loaded their 18 kids and all of their belongings into a big, old covered wagon and headed farther west. Just as the wagon was about to cross the Pecos River, the rear left wheel hit a great rock. All at once, one-year-old Bill bounced out of the wagon. He landed so hard in the desert dirt that the wind got knocked out of him and he couldn't cry out. No one could have heard him anyway. His brothers and sisters were making such a racket in the back of the wagon that it wasn't possible even to hear thunder. It was evening before anyone noticed that the baby was missing. By then, it was too late to do anything about it.

As the wagon disappeared into the distance, young Bill lay there watching it. Suddenly, an old coyote walked over. He sniffed the little boy a few times. Then the coyote picked the boy up by the scruff of his neck and carried him to his den.

So it happened that Bill came to live with the coyotes. The coyotes taught the boy everything they knew about the wild out-of-doors. He was educated in the fine art of hunting and learned the proper way to howl at the moon. By the time he was ten, he could outrun and outhowl any coyote in the Southwest. The boy completely forgot what it was like to be human. Until he was 17, he believed that he was a full-blooded coyote.

Then, one day, a cowboy came riding through the desert and saw the boy roaming about naked and dirty on all fours. The cowboy told Bill that he wasn't a coyote; he was a human being. Bill growled at this news, but deep in his heart he knew the man was right. He'd always suspected that he was different from the other coyotes. So, Pecos Bill said good-bye to all of his four-legged friends and thanked them for all they had taught him. Then he rode off with the cowboy toward his ranch.

At first, acting like a human wasn't easy for Pecos Bill. But he soon got the hang of it. In no time, he became the roughest, toughest cowboy of them all.

Finding Main Idea

1. What is the tall tale mostly about?
   - Ⓐ the life of a cowboy
   - Ⓑ Pecos Bill's days as a coyote
   - Ⓒ the ways of the coyote
   - Ⓓ Pecos Bill's adventures at a cattle ranch

Recalling Facts and Details

2. How old was Bill when he lost his family?
   - Ⓐ one
   - Ⓑ four
   - Ⓒ ten
   - Ⓓ 17

Understanding Sequence

3. What was the first thing that happened after Bill fell out of the wagon?
   - Ⓐ An old coyote brought the boy to his den.
   - Ⓑ He watched the wagon disappear.
   - Ⓒ An old coyote walked over to him.
   - Ⓓ He landed hard in the desert dirt.

Recognizing Cause and Effect

4. Bill's family didn't look for him because
   - Ⓐ the coyote carried him off immediately.
   - Ⓑ his brothers and sisters were making too much noise.
   - Ⓒ they didn't realize that he was missing until it was too late.
   - Ⓓ he didn't cry out when he fell out of the wagon.

Comparing and Contrasting

5. How was Pecos Bill different from other cowboys?
   - Ⓐ He used a lasso.
   - Ⓑ He came from eastern Texas.
   - Ⓒ He was rougher and tougher.
   - Ⓓ He was a full-blooded coyote.

Making Predictions

6. Predict what might have happened if Pecos Bill had not met the cowboy.
   - Ⓐ He would have still become a great cowboy.
   - Ⓑ He would have continued to live with the coyotes.
   - Ⓒ He would have left the coyotes anyway.
   - Ⓓ He would never have become a human being.

Finding Word Meaning in Context

7. In paragraph three, the word *scruff* means
   A "a scratch."
   B "to shuffle along."
   C "scent."
   D "the back of the neck."

Identifying Author's Purpose

10. The author probably wrote the tall tale to
    A describe the ways of the coyote.
    B explain what a cowboy does.
    C convince readers that Pecos Bill was the greatest cowboy who ever lived.
    D entertain readers with a story about a cowboy hero.

Drawing Conclusions and Making Inferences

8. The great cowboy was probably called Pecos Bill because he
   A got bounced out of the family wagon as it was about to cross the Pecos River.
   B was born near the Pecos River.
   C was as swift as the Pecos River.
   D asked the coyotes to name him after the nearby river.

Interpreting Figurative Language

11. In the last paragraph, the phrase *got the hang of it* means
    A "understood how something was hung."
    B "learned how to do something."
    C "spent time somewhere."
    D "kept trying."

Distinguishing Between Fact and Opinion

9. Which of these is an opinion?
   A Pecos Bill forgot what it was like to be human.
   B Pecos Bill taught cowboys how to round up cattle.
   C Pecos Bill was the roughest, toughest cowboy of them all.
   D Pecos Bill was educated in the fine art of hunting.

Summarizing

12. What is the best summary of the tall tale?
    A Pecos Bill was the greatest cowboy, and he taught the other cowboys everything they knew.
    B Pecos Bill grew up to become the best coyote in the Southwest.
    C Before he became a great cowboy, Pecos Bill grew up with the coyotes.
    D Pecos Bill lived with the coyotes during his youth.

Here is an article about the common cold. Read the article.
Then do Numbers 13 through 24.

The common cold is the most widespread of all illnesses. It affects the nose, throat, and, sometimes, the air passages and lungs. The first symptoms of a cold are usually a tickle in the throat, a runny or stuffy nose, and sneezing. Other symptoms may develop, such as watering eyes, a low fever, a sore throat, and a cough. A cold sufferer may also experience aching muscles, headaches, and chills. Adults usually catch at least one cold each year. Most children get at least two or three colds a year.

Colds are most frequent during the winter months. This fact has led many people to believe that colds are caused by cold, wet conditions. The true cause, however, is viruses. Viruses are germs that are easily passed from one person to another. Cold viruses are spread when a person with a cold coughs or sneezes. People catch a cold by breathing in the tiny droplets of moisture that have been sprayed into the air. They can also get a cold by handling objects that carry cold germs.

One reason that colds are more common in winter is that people tend to spend more time indoors in cold weather. Being in close contact with people for long periods of time makes it easier for cold viruses to be passed on.

Unlike many other illnesses, a cold can strike a person more than once. The reason that a person can catch many colds is that there are more than 200 different cold viruses. A person's body can build up protection against a virus that has already attacked it. But this immunity cannot help a person fight off a different cold virus that strikes.

No one has found a cure for the common cold, but some people think that a cure is close at hand. Presently, there are plenty of cold medicines for sale in drugstores. But all of these medicines treat only symptoms. They can relieve some of the discomfort a person with a cold suffers. Fortunately, most colds clear up within a week. Until then, people with colds should eat healthful foods and drink plenty of fluids.

People will try anything to prevent a cold. They may avoid cold drafts and dampness. Some may take large quantities of vitamin C. The best way to prevent a cold, however, is to stay away from people who have colds. That advice is cold comfort, though, for everyone who has to go to work and school.

Finding Main Idea

13. The best title for the article is
    Ⓐ "How Viruses Spread."
    Ⓑ "Health Myths."
    Ⓒ "Treating Cold Symptoms."
    Ⓓ "The Common Cold."

Recognizing Cause and Effect

16. Colds are more common in winter because
    Ⓐ viruses can live only in cold weather.
    Ⓑ people spend more time indoors and are more likely to come in contact with someone who has a cold.
    Ⓒ people sneeze and cough more in cold weather.
    Ⓓ cold viruses appear more often during cold months.

Recalling Facts and Details

14. How many colds do most children get each year?
    Ⓐ one
    Ⓑ one or two
    Ⓒ two or three
    Ⓓ three or more

Comparing and Contrasting

17. How is the common cold different from many other illnesses?
    Ⓐ It can strike more than once.
    Ⓑ It can strike only once.
    Ⓒ It is caused by a virus.
    Ⓓ It can be easily caught.

Understanding Sequence

15. Which of these cold symptoms appears first?
    Ⓐ aching muscles
    Ⓑ runny nose
    Ⓒ cough
    Ⓓ sore throat

Making Predictions

18. Predict how things would be different if there were a cure for the common cold.
    Ⓐ No one would ever have a sore throat again.
    Ⓑ Drugstores would go out of business.
    Ⓒ People would spend more time outdoors.
    Ⓓ People would miss fewer days of work and school each year.

Finding Word Meaning in Context

19. In paragraph four, the best meaning of the word *immunity* is
    - Ⓐ "a way to keep sick people away from healthy people."
    - Ⓑ "the body's ability to fight off disease."
    - Ⓒ "a drug given to people to protect them against disease."
    - Ⓓ "the spread of a disease."

Identifying Author's Purpose

22. What was the author's main purpose in writing the article?
    - Ⓐ to give information about the common cold
    - Ⓑ to describe symptoms of the common cold
    - Ⓒ to persuade readers to avoid people with colds
    - Ⓓ to entertain readers with myths about the common cold

Drawing Conclusions and Making Inferences

20. From the article, you can tell that
    - Ⓐ older people are more likely to catch a cold.
    - Ⓑ people never catch colds in the summer.
    - Ⓒ cold viruses spread more easily among children than adults.
    - Ⓓ people can prevent colds by spending time outdoors.

Interpreting Figurative Language

23. In the last paragraph, what does the phrase *cold comfort* mean?
    - Ⓐ "uninterested in relief"
    - Ⓑ "comfortable despite cold temperatures"
    - Ⓒ "something to help a sick person feel more comfortable"
    - Ⓓ "no relief at all"

Distinguishing Between Fact and Opinion

21. Which of these is a fact?
    - Ⓐ People will do anything to prevent a cold.
    - Ⓑ The common cold is the most widespread of all illnesses.
    - Ⓒ There is no illness worse than a cold.
    - Ⓓ People with colds should be kind enough to avoid contact with others.

Summarizing

24. What is the best summary of the article?
    - Ⓐ The common cold affects the nose, throat, and, sometimes, the air passages and lungs.
    - Ⓑ The search for the common cold continues.
    - Ⓒ The common cold is the most widespread of all illnesses, is caused by viruses, and has no cure.
    - Ⓓ The most popular myth about the common cold is that it is caused by cold, wet conditions.

Here is a biography of a great American. Read the biography.
Then do Numbers 25 through 36.

He is one of the most respected men in United States history. He was a printer, a writer, a publisher, a scientist, an inventor, and a government leader. Who was this remarkable man? Benjamin Franklin, of course.

Benjamin Franklin was born on January 17, 1706, in Boston. He was the fifteenth of 17 children born to Josiah and Abiah Franklin. Ben was a smart child, but his family was poor. At age ten, he had to leave school to help his father in his candle and soap shop. At age 12, Ben became an apprentice, or student worker, in a printing shop run by his half-brother James. Although Ben enjoyed his work, he did not like his older brother. So, at age 17, he ran away to Philadelphia. There he quickly found work as a printer.

Franklin was a hard worker. Within five years, he opened his own print shop. There he started his own newspaper and published *Poor Richard's Almanac*. This yearly calendar contained all kinds of facts, weather forecasts, and wise and witty sayings. Here are a few of his most famous sayings:

Early to bed and early to rise, makes a man healthy, wealthy, and wise.
An ounce of prevention is worth a pound of cure.
A penny saved is a penny earned.

As busy as he was with his printing business, Franklin also helped to make Philadelphia a better city. He set up the first lending library, the first fire department, and the first post office. He also helped establish a school that later became the University of Pennsylvania.

By age 42, Franklin's hard work and success had made him a rich man, so he retired and turned his attention to science. By sending up a kite during a storm, Franklin proved that lightning is a form of electricity. He had attached a key to the kite's string. When a lightning bolt struck the kite, the key became charged with electricity. Franklin then put his discovery to use by inventing the lightning rod. He also invented the Franklin stove, bifocal eyeglasses, and the harmonica.

Franklin is probably remembered most for his role in helping to build our nation. He was the first person to present the idea of uniting the 13 colonies. He spent 15 years in England trying to persuade the king to govern the colonies more fairly. In 1776, he signed the Declaration of Independence. During the Revolutionary War, he went to France and convinced the French to send troops and supplies to the colonists. He helped write the peace treaty that ended the war. He also helped to create the Constitution of the United States.

Benjamin Franklin lived long enough to see the Constitution become the basic law of the United States. He died on April 17, 1790, at age 84.

Finding Main Idea

25. What is the main idea of the biography?
    - (A) Ben Franklin lived long enough to see the birth of the United States.
    - (B) Ben Franklin was one of the most remarkable men in United States history.
    - (C) Ben Franklin was a hard worker.
    - (D) Ben Franklin was a poor boy who became a rich man.

Recognizing Cause and Effect

28. Why did Franklin retire from printing at age 42?
    - (A) He wanted to make Philadelphia a better city.
    - (B) He was rich and wanted to turn his attention to science.
    - (C) He wanted to prove that lightning is a form of electricity.
    - (D) He wanted to play a role in building our nation.

Recalling Facts and Details

26. How many children were there in Franklin's family?
    - (A) 12
    - (B) 15
    - (C) 16
    - (D) 17

Comparing and Contrasting

29. How were young Ben Franklin and old Ben Franklin alike?
    - (A) They both were hard workers who achieved a lot.
    - (B) They both wished they had more schooling.
    - (C) They were both interested in politics.
    - (D) They were both poor.

Understanding Sequence

27. What happened immediately after Franklin went to Philadelphia?
    - (A) He became an apprentice in his half-brother's shop.
    - (B) He published *Poor Richard's Almanac*.
    - (C) He found work as a printer.
    - (D) He opened his own print shop.

Making Predictions

30. What might have happened if Franklin had stayed in the printing business?
    - (A) He would never have become rich.
    - (B) He would not have had much time for his interest in science.
    - (C) The Revolutionary War would have begun sooner.
    - (D) The Declaration of Independence would not exist.

Finding Word Meaning in Context

31. In paragraph four, the word *establish* means

    Ⓐ "set up."

    Ⓑ "prove beyond a doubt."

    Ⓒ "try or attempt."

    Ⓓ "predict."

Identifying Author's Purpose

34. The biography was written mainly to

    Ⓐ tell readers about a great American.

    Ⓑ persuade readers to work as hard as Franklin.

    Ⓒ entertain readers with humorous stories about Franklin.

    Ⓓ describe the printing business in the 1700s.

Drawing Conclusions and Making Inferences

32. From this biography, you can tell that

    Ⓐ Franklin wanted to be president of the United States.

    Ⓑ Franklin was not a happy man.

    Ⓒ people thought that Franklin was a strange man.

    Ⓓ Franklin liked to explore new ideas and activities.

Interpreting Figurative Language

35. The saying *A penny saved is a penny earned* probably means that

    Ⓐ a person should save every penny that is earned.

    Ⓑ a person who does not work will never have any savings.

    Ⓒ money that is saved has the same value as money that is earned.

    Ⓓ one penny is not worth as much as two pennies.

Distinguishing Between Fact and Opinion

33. Which of these is an opinion about Ben Franklin?

    Ⓐ He was the first person to present the idea of uniting the 13 colonies.

    Ⓑ By age 42, he was a rich man.

    Ⓒ He was the most important founder of the United States.

    Ⓓ He proved that lightning is a form of electricity.

Summarizing

36. Which of these is the best summary of the biography?

    Ⓐ Ben Franklin was a poor boy who became a rich man.

    Ⓑ Ben Franklin was one of the greatest leaders in American history.

    Ⓒ Ben Franklin was a man who achieved much in his lifetime.

    Ⓓ Ben Franklin changed careers many times during his long life.

ACKNOWLEDGMENTS

Curriculum Associates wishes to thank the following authors and publishers
for their permission to reprint copyrighted material. Every effort has been made
to locate all copyright holders. Any errors or omissions in copyright notice
are inadvertent and will be credited in future printings as they are discovered.

page 11:   *THE MAN IN THE MOON: Sky Tales from Many Lands* by Alta Jablow
             and Carl Withers, illustrated by Peggy Wilson. Text copyright © 1969
             by Alta Jablow and Carl Withers. Illustrations copyright, © 1969 by Peggy
             Wilson. Reprinted by permission of Henry Holt and Company, LLC.

page 47:   "The Heron and the Hummingbird," from *FEATHERS AND TAILS* by
             David Kherdian, illustrated by Nonny Hogrogian. Copyright © 1992
             by David Kherdian, text. Copyright © 1992 by Nonny Hogrogian,
             illustrations. Used by permission of Philomel Books, a division of
             Penguin Putnam Inc.

page 61:   "The Hoja," from *Aramco World*, Vol. 48, No. 5. Reprinted by
             permission of Aramco World, Escondido, California.

page 69:   "Seeing Snow" by Gustavo Pérez Firmat from *Bilingual Blues*.
             Copyright 1995 by Bilingual Press/Editorial Bilingüe. Reprinted
             by permission of the publisher Bilingual Press/Editorial Bilingüe,
             Arizona State University, Tempe, Arizona.

page 88:   "Holding Up the Sky" is from *Peace Tales: World Folktales to Talk About*
             © 1992 by Margaret Read MacDonald. Reprinted by permission of
             Linnet Books/The Shoe String Press, Inc., North Haven, Connecticut.

page 114:   "Can Opener Lures Lost Cat Home," Associated Press Wire Services.
             Courtesy of Associated Press.

Illustration Credits

Hilarie Crosman/page 28

Mary Newell DePalma/page 56

Susan Hawk/pages 6, 11, 14, 21, 24, 30, 48, 50, 62, 73, 88, 90, 98, 100, 106, 110,
             112, 114, 116, 119

Jamie Ruh/page 4

Photography Credits

Corbis/Peter Johnson/page 18

Corbis/Library of Congress/page 25

Corbis/Phil Schermeister/page 45

Courtesy of McDonald's Corporation/page 27

Courtesy of Jerry Search/Southern California Speed Skating Association/page 46

Courtesy of Gustavo Pérez Firmat/page 69

Courtesy of National Baseball Hall of Fame Library, Cooperstown, New York/page 80

Portrait Gallery/Perry-Castañeda Library, University of Texas at Austin/pages 104 and 122

Peter Veit/NGS Image Collection/page 58

Tony Stone Images/Patrick Ward/page 102

www.arttoday.com/pages 8, 12, 17, 22, 32, 34, 37, 38, 40, 45, 55, 60, 67, 70, 78, 86, 93, and 108

Developer and Writer: Joan Krensky

Developer and Editor: Deborah Adcock

Designer: Jamie Ruh